Computer-oriented Mathematics

Computer-oriented Mathematics

An introduction to numerical methods

by Ladis D. Kovach, Pepperdine College

Holden-Day

San Francisco, Cambridge, London, Amsterdam

Third printing: June 1969

Library of Congress Catalog Card No. 64–21711

Printed in the United States of America

Preface

This book is about *mathematics*. Although the word "computer" appears in the title, you will not find any *details* about computers nor will you learn a computer language.

You will be introduced, however, to a fascinating and useful branch of mathematics—numerical mathematics—which is concerned with solving problems—*difficult* problems, not the innocuous problems found in the average book on mathematics.

Yet the background necessary to understand the methods presented here is quite modest. The completion of two or three years of high-school mathematics—with a modern flavor—is sufficient. Thus this book will appeal to the high-school and college student who seeks to learn more about solving nonlinear problems. It will also be useful to the educated layman who wishes to learn about various mathematical techniques that are especially adapted to computers.

In brief, you will be introduced to some unusual mathematics that is almost never taught in standard courses. You will become acquainted with the frontiers of numerical mathematics and may even find that you can make a contribution that will extend our present knowledge.

Computer-oriented Mathematics presents *new* ideas, *exciting* ideas, even *romantic* ideas. It does this by showing how computational speed can be traded for mathematical sophistication. This may seem like a difficult trade, but the success of the modern electronic computer is due to the mathematician's ingenuity in discovering ways to make this trade.

L. D. K.

Table of Contents

To My Students

Introduction

It was fashionable some years ago to refer to computers as "giant brains." The only justification that can be given for using this term is that it did serve to bring computers to the attention of the public. However, linking the words "brain" and "machine" was very misleading. The implication was that man had succeeded, to some extent, in building a replica of himself.

Science fiction writers and some philosophers immediately got on the band wagon and a large number of articles and debates ensued. We find such intriguing titles as "Can Machines Think?" "Electronic Computers—Slave or Master?" "Self-Reproducing Machines," "Design for a Brain," "Mechanized Reasoning," and so forth.

Gradually, as our understanding of computing machines increased, we realized that many of the stories about computers were pure flights of fancy. We suspect that computers cannot "think" nor are they "brains" in the usual sense of the word. We believe that computers cannot, in themselves, extend scientific knowledge or do original research.

If this appears to remove the exciting aspect of computers, rest assured that this is not the case. We will show that computers are responsible for new methods which are both useful and interesting. We will show you some new and exciting developments in mathematics which are the direct result of the widespread use of computers. You will see some of the advances that have been made as man continues to use his intellect in order to modify his environment.

The main purpose of this book is to show how mathematics has bridged the gap between the human and the machine. That a gap does exist is evident if we examine a large electronic digital computer in greater detail. When we do this, we find that basically all a computer can do is *count*. Of course, it does this at such great speed that some people refer to computers as "supersonic morons," a more realistic name than "giant brains," because it conveys an idea of the machine's high speed and narrow mathematical ability.

Now if we call a computer a supersonic moron, we have to call a mathematician a "deliberate genius." This name emphasizes the fact that humans have a high intelligence but are limited when it comes to calculating speed.

Thus we have a definite mismatch between the mathematician and the computer. The first understands mathematics but is slow while the second knows no mathematics but is fast. This incompatibility can be illustrated by Figure 1. The multi-pronged plug represents the mathematician. He is capable of

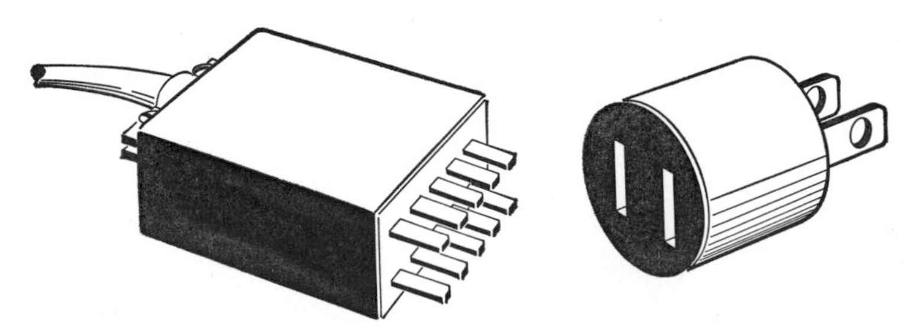

Fig. 1. Mismatch between man and computer. Multi-pronged plug (left) represents the mathematician's complex responses to stimulation. Two-pronged plug (right) represents the computer's limited ability.

receiving inputs (or stimulation) of various types, operating on this information in a complex manner and giving an output (or response) which may take a number of forms. The double plug represents the computer. It can only accept information limited in quantity and type, it can operate on information in only a simple manner, and its output is somewhat limited.

It should be apparent, then, that in order for information to flow from the human to the machine, it is necessary to provide an adapter. We may think of this adapter as a black box that has many receptacles on one side to accommodate the human multi-plug and two prongs on the other side to fit the computer plug. When we consider the function of the adapter we realize that there is an air of mystery surrounding this black box. This book is an attempt to remove that mystery and to describe in some detail the operation of the adapter.

We hesitate to give a name to the adapter plug in our analogy because no single name can describe it adequately. We could call it the "numerical analysis adapter" because mathematicians use numerical analysis in order to communicate with computers. However, this term may be somewhat restrictive so it seems appropriate to call the mysterious black box simply "computer-oriented mathematics."

Any mathematics that enables us to communicate with a computer can be classified as computer-oriented mathematics. You will discover that many of the methods that fall into this category are not new, but before the advent of computers they had only limited utility. Some methods are clever adaptations of techniques which have been known for thousands of years. Mathematicians have rediscovered processes that are particularly suited to a computer's capabilities. They have also devised new and unusual kinds of mathematics in certain cases.

In some cases the limitations of the computer have necessitated the development of new mathematical techniques. Often these have stood on their own and superseded former methods because they were more logical, hence easier to learn.

The ingenuity demonstrated by mathematicians in evolving

ways to reduce extremely complex operations to simple ones is remarkable. An account of the details is a fascinating story of modern developments in mathematics.

Perhaps the greatest value of this book lies in the fact that it will show you new methods for attacking complex problems. And the best part is that most of these methods do not require your having access to a computer. You will not even need a desk calculator! The simple operations can be carried out with pencil and paper. Hence in a limited way you can actually go through the same processes that are used in large computers to solve problems.

This will give you not only a greater understanding of the ways in which computers operate but it will also give you an appreciation of the value of their great speed. Finally, you will be introduced to some of the thought processes used by numerical analysts — the mathematicians who reduce difficult problems to a series of simple ones. You may even discover some problem-solving methods yourself as you read along.

1. Characteristics of Digital Computers

In order to understand some of the mathematical techniques to be described and in order to provide some motivation for their study it is necessary to know something about digital computers. One might well say that it is not necessary to know the details of a desk calculator—a simple example of a digital computer—in order to use one. However, we are not so much interested in finding out how to use a digital computer as we are in appreciating the way mathematics has been re-oriented in order to be compatible with the capabilities of the computer.

A modern, large-scale, electronic, digital computer may be thought of as a machine that can count very rapidly. You can imagine a counter such as the mileage indicator of an automobile, except that there are spaces for perhaps 20 digits. At the start the counter has a string of zeros all the way across. Now, if we enter the number 5 into the machine, one of the counters (the one on the extreme right) spins until it stops at 5. If next we enter the number 7, the indication changes to 12 and we have performed a simple addition. We can continue to enter numbers and the counter will show the accumulated total until such time as we set the counter to zero and start over.

When entering larger numbers in the counter it is not necessary to *count* to that number in order. Each place assumes the correct position very quickly. For example, the number 625 can be put into the counter by placing the 6, the 2, and the 5 *simultaneously* in the proper positions. In this respect the counter—or accumulator as it is called—is *not* analogous to the automobile's mileage indicator.

The preceding example, of course, is an over-simplified description, because we have not said anything about how the numbers are entered into the counter, what happens to the total after it is obtained, how we reset the counter, etc. Fortunately, for our present purposes these are details which we may ignore. Those who have an interest in these matters can find references to other works in the bibliography.

For the present we have the fact that a computer is capable of counting at extremely high speeds.[1] Some idea of the speed can be obtained when we say that a computer can add two numbers in approximately 72 one-millionths of a second. These need not be simple numbers like 5 and 7 but each may consist of, say, twenty digits. The counters spin and the result is obtained in the same fraction of a second. Think of it, almost *fourteen thousand* additions in one second!

This all sounds fine but so far we have nothing more than a glorified adding machine. Next we mention that the counters are capable of going *backward* as well as *forward*. We have now added *subtraction* to the computer's talents because if we start with 12 and count backward 7, we will reach 5. The operation of subtraction is done with the same speed as addition.

[1] The development of computers is proceeding so rapidly that any figures we might give concerning their speed would be obsolete by the time the type was set and the book printed. Hence we are giving figures which are *typical* of many computers in use at this time. In no way are these figures to be considered as maximum speeds.

Let us anticipate one of the limitations of the computer which led to a unique method of subtraction. If we had 5 entered in the counter and instructed the computer to subtract 12, the counter would run backward and we would expect to see something like the following:

9	9	9	9	9	9	9	9	9	9	9	9	9	9	9	9	9	9	9	3

Later we will discuss how this is interpreted as -7.

Since the computer can add, it can also multiply. To multiply 8 by 6 it is only necessary to add six groups each consisting of 8. In other words, multiplication is *repeated addition.* It stands to reason that multiplication is somewhat slower than addition for this reason. A typical multiplication may take 288 one-millionths of a second. One would expect multiplication to be much slower than this but the computer designers have developed special ways of speeding up the process.

One way to speed up the process of multiplication is to combine repeated addition with shifting. This can be illustrated with a simple example. Suppose we wish to multiply 237 by 45. It would be far too slow to add forty-five 237's. Instead we make use of the fact that the required product can be generated by using the distributive property as follows:

$$\begin{aligned} 237 \times 45 &= 237 \times (40 + 5) \\ &= 237 \times 40 + 237 \times 5 \\ &= 2370 \times 4 + 237 \times 5 . \end{aligned}$$

Hence we can accomplish the multiplication by adding five 237's and four 2370's. The number 2370 can be obtained from 237 by shifting the digits one place to the left.

Finally, the computer can perform division since this can be done by *repeated subtraction.* In fact, when we divide 3457 by 23 using long division, we keep subtracting multiples of 23 from 3457 until the remainder is less than 23. It is interesting to note that this process need not be done in a systematic manner. Different paths all lead to the same result. For example:

$$3457 \div 23 = ?$$

This is an arbitrary guess of the quotient: $= 100$

This is a multiple of 23, namely 100×23: $\underline{2300}$

This is a remainder: 1157

This is an "educated" guess: $= 50$

This is another multiple of 23; namely 50×23: $\underline{1150}$

This is the final remainder: 7

We would then add our guesses and write the quotient. The complete division problem would look as follows:

$$\begin{array}{rccc}
3457 & \div\ 23 & = & \underline{\underline{150\frac{7}{23}}} \\
-\underline{2300} & & & 100 \\
1157 & & & \\
-\underline{1150} & & & 50 \\
7 & & &
\end{array}$$

Another person may have the following result:

$$\begin{array}{rccc}
3457 & \div\ 23 & = & \underline{\underline{150\frac{7}{23}}} \\
-\underline{2300} & & & 100 \\
1157 & & & \\
-\underline{\ 920} & & & 40 \\
237 & & & \\
-\underline{\ 230} & & & 10 \\
7 & & &
\end{array}$$

The computer, of course, does not perform division in a *random* manner as the last two examples might indicate, but rather in a *systematic* manner. As in the case of multiplication, division is accomplished by combining subtraction and shifting operations.

Thus the digital computer, chiefly by "counting," can perform addition, subtraction, multiplication, and division. In short, it can do fifth-grade arithmetic but at a speed that can hardly be comprehended by a fifth-grader.

We seem to have run out of talent at this point and it is reasonable to ask, "What about other operations in mathematics? How can the computer extract square root, for example?" Again as a preview of other similar things to come, let us examine a method of extracting square root.

Suppose we wish to find $\sqrt{25}$. One way is to subtract from 25 the successive odd integers, 1, 3, 5, $\cdots$ until we reach zero. For example,

$$25 - 1 - 3 - 5 - 7 - 9 = 0 .$$

We note that we have subtracted *five* odd integers but we hesitate to jump to conclusions at this point. To strengthen our conjecture we try $\sqrt{49}$:

$$49 - 1 - 3 - 5 - 7 - 9 - 11 - 13 = 0 .$$

This time we subtracted *seven* odd integers and we are becoming more jubilant. In an adventurous manner we try $\sqrt{39}$.

$$39 - 1 - 3 - 5 - 7 - 9 - 11 = 3 .$$

We see that we have subtracted *six* odd integers but did not quite reach zero. We might conclude that $\sqrt{39}$ is more than 6.

To remove any doubt about the validity of the method we point out that it is well-known that the sum of the first n odd integers is n^2. In symbols,

$$1 + 3 + 5 + 7 + \cdots + (2n - 1) = n^2 .$$

This identity can be proved in elementary algebra, being a simple exercise in mathematical induction.

Notice that finding the square root of a number as described above consisted of *subtracting* odd integers and then *counting* how many integers were subtracted. Both of these operations fall within the capabilities of the digital computer. If we had to evaluate $\sqrt{12.3}$ we could proceed as follows:

$$1230 - 1 - 3 - 5 - 7 - \cdots - 67 - 69 = 5.$$

Here we have subtracted a total of *thirty-five* odd integers so we could say $\sqrt{12.3} = 3.5+$. In a similar manner we could obtain the square root to any desired accuracy.

Although this method seems to be ideally suited to the computer it is not used because it is wasteful of machine time. Moreover, mathematicians are generally not fond of methods which cannot be generalized. If we had to find the *cube* root of a number we would have to look for some other identity than the above one to use. Later we will discuss other methods of finding the square root of a number—methods which are more suitable because they are less time-consuming and more easily generalized.

Before closing this very brief description of the digital computer, we should mention one more of its capabilities; this is the ability to *compare* two numbers. It turns out that this is a most important ability. In the square root problem, for example, the computer must know when to *stop* subtracting odd integers and *start* counting the number of odd integers it has subtracted. It does this by comparing the difference each time with zero. When the difference ceases to be greater than zero, *that* is the time to stop subtracting and start counting.

It is important to realize that this is a *decision* the computer must make rather than the operator since the operator does not know the answer ahead of time. Perhaps because of its ability to make such decisions, the computer has been endowed with human-like powers.

Exercises

1. If multiplication is performed as repeated addition and shifting, how many additions are required to find the product of 2379 and 645?

2. By subtracting successive odd integers estimate $\sqrt{75}$.
3. Find $\sqrt{75}$ correct to one decimal place by using the method of this chapter.
4. Notice the pattern in the following:

$$
\begin{aligned}
1^3 &= 1^2 \\
1^3 + 2^3 &= 3^2 \\
1^3 + 2^3 + 3^3 &= 6^2 \\
1^3 + 2^3 + 3^3 + 4^3 &= 10^2 \\
1^3 + 2^3 + 3^3 + 4^3 + 5^3 &= 15^2 \\
1^3 + 2^3 + 3^3 + 4^3 + 5^3 + 6^3 &= 21^2 \\
1^3 + 2^3 + 3^3 + 4^3 + 5^3 + 6^3 + 7^3 &= 28^2
\end{aligned}
$$

Devise a method for finding $\sqrt{784}$.

5. Use the method suggested by exercise 4 to find $\sqrt{495}$. Estimate as closely as you can.
6. What advantages does the method for finding square root given in this chapter have over the method of exercise 4?

2. Various Number Bases

The early digital computers used the *decimal* system of numeration. This is the commonly used system which consists of ten distinct symbols, namely,

$$0, 1, 2, 3, 4, 5, 6, 7, 8, 9\,.$$

By placing these symbols in various positions we can represent any number we please. The position of the numeral determines the particular power of ten that multiplies the numeral.

As an example, the number 3784 represents the sum

$$3 \times 10^3 + 7 \times 10^2 + 8 \times 10^1 + 4 \times 10^0\,.$$

Decimal fractions can be represented by extending this system. The number 0.6052 is a short, convenient way of writing the sum

$$6 \times 10^{-1} + 0 \times 10^{-2} + 5 \times 10^{-3} + 2 \times 10^{-4}\,.$$

As another example, the number 190.58 is a way of writing the sum

$$1 \times 10^2 + 9 \times 10^1 + 0 \times 10^0 + 5 \times 10^{-1} + 8 \times 10^{-2}\,.$$

Note that the coefficients of the various powers of ten must be one of our ten numerals while the exponents may be *any* integer—positive, negative, or zero.

It very soon became apparent that the design of a computer was difficult because of the necessity of keeping track of ten different numerals. However, thanks to the pioneering work of Leibniz,[1] who had no idea how widespread his number system would become, computer designers were able to use the *binary* system.

In this system there are only two numerals, 0 and 1. Instead of powers of *ten*, we now have powers of *two*. A typical number in this system is written as 1011011. In order that there be no misunderstanding about which base we're using, we usually write this number as $(1011011)_2$. As before, this is a convenient way of expressing the sum

$$1 \times 2^6 + 0 \times 2^5 + 1 \times 2^4 + 1 \times 2^3 + 0 \times 2^2 + 1 \times 2^1 + 1 \times 2^0 .$$

We can evaluate this sum in the decimal system and obtain the decimal equivalent of the given binary number, namely,

$$64 + 0 + 16 + 8 + 0 + 2 + 1 = 91 .$$

Hence

$$(1011011)_2 = (91)_{10} .$$

It may appear that we haven't gained anything because in the above example it requires seven digits to represent a number in binary notation that can be represented by two digits in decimal notation. The fact is that having only the numerals 0 and 1 makes our arithmetic extremely simple. Instead of a long multiplication table that takes weeks to learn, we have the following:

[1] Gottfried Wilhelm Leibniz (1646–1716), a German mathematician, was one of the inventors of the calculus. He also invented a calculating machine which was capable of adding, subtracting, multiplying, dividing, and extracting roots.

×	0	1
1	0	1
0	0	0

Addition is only slightly more complicated but all the necessary facts are included in the following table:

+	0	1
0	0	1
1	1	10

As one mathematician put it, "In the binary system we count on our fists instead of our fingers!"

Using the binary system made it possible to design computers that were much more efficient and rapid. Now the orientation of the magnetic field about a tiny coil could be used to represent the two situations. If the field was oriented one way, it represented 0; if oriented the opposite way, 1. Many numbers could be put on a small piece of magnetic tape. If the tape contained a tiny spot that was magnetized in one direction, this represented 1; a spot magnetized in the other direction stood for 0. In short, the binary system simplified the electrical design and made it possible to make significant advances in computer design.

Perhaps the most familiar computer accessory is the punched card. This is a card that can be coded in such a way that a hole represents "one" and no hole represents "zero." Place value can be indicated by designating a certain *location* on the card.

Counting (or addition) proceeds in an orderly manner in that when we have used all our numerals in a given place, the next highest place value is increased by one and we start over. This is illustrated by the following table which shows how to count in the binary system.

Decimal	Binary	Decimal	Binary
0	0	13	1101
1	1	14	1110
2	10	15	1111
3	11	16	10000
4	100	17	10001
5	101	18	10010
6	110	19	10011
7	111	20	10100
8	1000	21	10101
9	1001	22	10110
10	1010	23	10111
11	1011	24	11000
12	1100	25	11001
		etc.	

Note that the binary number 111 is *similar* to the decimal 999. In both cases all three places contain the "last" numeral in the system so that the next counting number in both cases is 1000.

Because of this uniformity in counting, even illiterate people are able to do sums. Although subtraction is the inverse of addition and can theoretically be accomplished simply by counting backwards, the subtraction of one digit from a smaller digit requires that the minuend be regrouped. Since the binary system contains only zeros and ones, it is necessary to regroup much more often than in the decimal system.

As an example, consider the following exercise in subtraction:

```
                                                 110
                                                10
1 0 0 1 1                                      1̸ 0̸ 0̸ 1 1
−   1 1 0   which becomes after regrouping     −   1 1 0
---------                                      ---------
                                                 1 1 0 1
```

One simple way out of this difficulty is to *increase* the subtrahend instead of *diminishing* the digits of the minuend. This leads to a different concept of subtraction which is shown by the following example:

```
    1 1
  1 Ø Ø 1 1
−     1̸ 1 0
    1̸ 0
  1 0
  ---------
  0 1 1 0 1
```

We were able to subtract the two rightmost digits without any trouble but when we came to the third digit from the right we couldn't subtract 1 from 0. Hence we *added* to the subtrahend *and* to the minuend (in order not to change the problem). At this stage we had

```
    1
1 0 Ø 1 1
    1̸ 1 0
  1 0
---------
    1 0 1
```

Now the same situation exists in the fourth place from the right and is handled in the same manner.

Another way of accomplishing subtraction is by means of a process called *complementation.* In the decimal system we can subtract 6 from 9 by counting backward starting at 9 until we have counted 6 and arrived at 3. We can also start with 9 and count forward until we reach 13. If we ignore the numeral 1 in 13 we get the required number but we get it by counting forward 4. Thus we say that 4 is the ten's complement of 6. A number and its ten's complement always add to some power of 10. For example, the ten's complement of 32 is 68, of 187 is 813, etc.

Using this idea, we can subtract two numbers by finding the complement of the subtrahend and adding it to the minuend, being sure to ignore the extraneous 1. The following example illustrates the procedure:

$$\begin{array}{r} 3865 \\ -1781 \\ \hline \end{array} \quad \text{becomes} \quad \begin{array}{r} 3865 \\ +\ 8219 \\ \hline \not{1}2084 \end{array} \quad \text{(ten's complement of 1781)}$$

There is a slight variation of the above method which is even more useful. It is called the "minus-one complement" and the "nine's complement." In this method the complement of a number is obtained not by subtracting it from a power of 10 but from a row of 9's which is much easier to do. Thus the nine's complement of 7 is 2, of 23 is 76, of 489 is 510, etc. Although it's easier to find the complement this way, the result we get will be in error by one—hence the name, "minus-one complement." In order to use this method we must add one, in addition to ignoring the one in the leftmost digit.

$$\begin{array}{r} 5876 \\ -3719 \\ \hline \end{array} \quad \text{becomes} \quad \begin{array}{r} 5876 \\ 6280 \\ \hline \not{1}2156 \\ +1 \\ \hline 2157 \end{array} \quad \text{(minus-one complement)}$$

Since the "1" has been shifted from the left to the right, this idea is known as an "end-around carry."

Let us go back to the example in the first chapter where we subtracted 12 from 5 and ended up with a counter that registered as follows:

9	9	9	9	9	9	9	9	9	9	9	9	9	9	9	9	9	9	9	3

When the counter runs backward and passes zero so that we get a result like the above, we can replace this number by its ten's complement with a negative sign prefixed, i.e., by -7.

It is possible to extend the complement method of subtraction to other number bases using the equivalent of a row of 9's in the number system under consideration. In the binary system the method of complementation is especially useful and simplifies the process of subtraction considerably. The minus-one complement of a binary number is obtained by changing all the 1's to 0's and all the 0's to 1's. This is illustrated in the following example:

$$\begin{array}{rcrl} 11010 & & 11010 & \\ -\underline{1011} & \text{becomes} & +\underline{0100} & \text{minus-one complement of } 1011 \\ & & \cancel{1}1110 & \\ & & \underline{+1} & \\ & & 1111 & \end{array}$$

As a practical compromise between the unwieldy decimal system and the simple binary system which requires many digits to represent a number, many computers are built to use the *octal* system. This system uses the numerals 0, 1, 2, 3, 4, 5, 6, 7 and place values are powers of *eight*. For example,

$$\begin{aligned} (3671)_8 &= 3 \times 8^3 + 6 \times 8^2 + 7 \times 8^1 + 1 \times 8^0 \\ &= 1536 + 384 + 56 + 1 \\ &= (1977)_{10}\,. \end{aligned}$$

A subtraction would proceed as follows:

$$\begin{array}{rlr} 3651 & 7777 & 3651 \\ \underline{-2745} & \underline{-2745} & +\underline{5032} \\ & 5032 & \cancel{1}0703 \\ & \text{minus-one} & \underline{+1} \\ & \text{complement} & 704 \\ & \text{of } 2745 & \end{array}$$

Note that in adding the minus-one complement we had to add 5 and 3. Although this sum is 8 we could not write 8 because that numeral is not used in the octal system but is expressed as 10.

As a historical sidelight on number systems, a few primitive tribes of Australia and Africa use a very limited form of a binary, *ternary* (base 3) or *quaternary* (base 4) system. The *quinary* (base 5) system is still used by natives in New Hebrides. It is generally thought that the widespread use of the decimal system is a result of man's having ten fingers. In uncivilized countries, however, spears must be carried at all times as protection against unfriendly tribesmen and even more unfriendly animals. Thus only five fingers are available for counting purposes. This may account for the use of the quinary system in New Hebrides. The ancient Babylonians used both base 10 and *sexagesimal* (base 60) systems. Vestiges of the latter are found in our time and angle units of measurement. The Mayas of Yucatan use the *vigesimal* (base 20) system possibly because they prefer to count on their toes as well as their fingers. We sometimes measure things by the *score*, that is, by twenties.

The development of digital computers has given us a new appreciation and a greater understanding of various number systems. It has also opened up new fields for research and speculation. A number of unique number systems have been proposed recently and while they do not all appear to be practical at first glance, they have led mathematicians into new fields of thought.

When George Bergman was twelve years old and a student in junior high school he submitted a paper to Mathematics Magazine.[2] In this paper he described a number system whose base was the irrational number $(1 + \sqrt{5})/2$ which was known to the ancient Greeks as the "golden section." Bergman gives the rules for performing the operations of arithmetic in this system and shows how to convert numbers to and from this base.

Other systems have been proposed with a view to improving the efficiency of automatic computing. For example, keeping track of positive and negative numbers is a nuisance. Two suggestions have been made which would eliminate signed numbers.

One of these is to use a number system based on -2, since odd powers of this number are negative and even powers are positive.[3] For example, $(101101)_{-2}$ would represent -35 since

[2] Bergman, George: "A Number System with an Irrational Base," *Mathematics Magazine* (31), No. 2, pp. 98–110, Nov.–Dec. 1957.

[3] Wadell, Louis B.: "Negative Base Number Systems", *IRE Trans. of the Prof. Group on Elec. Comp.* (EC-6), No. 2, p. 123, June 1957.

$$1 \times (-2)^5 + 0 \times (-2)^4 + 1 \times (-2)^3 + 1 \times (-2)^2 + 0 \times (-2)^1 + 1 \times (-2)^0 = (-35)_{10}.$$

Similarly, $(10011)_{-2}$ represents $(+15)_{10}$ and $(1.11)_{-2}$ represents $(+0.75)_{10}$. In this system a separate sign indication is not required since the sign is self-contained. The following table shows a comparison of this system with the decimal system:

Negative	Number	Positive
0	zero	0
11	one	1
10	two	110
1101	three	111
1100	four	100
1111	five	101
1110	six	11010
1001	seven	11011
1000	eight	11000
1011	nine	11001
1010	ten	11110
110101	eleven	11111
110100	twelve	11100

Notice that negative numbers have an even number of digits while positive numbers have an odd number.

Another number system worthy of consideration is one that might be called a balanced ternary system.[4] It uses the digits minus one ($\bar{1}$), zero (0), and plus one (1). The following table shows how this system works:

Negative	Number	Positive
0	zero	0
$\bar{1}$	one	1
$\bar{1}$ 1	two	1 $\bar{1}$

[4] Reid, J. B.: Letter to the Editor, *Comm. Assoc. Comp. Mach.* (3), No. 3, pp. A12–13, March 1960.

$\bar{1}\ 0$	three	$1\ 0$
$\bar{1}\ \bar{1}$	four	$1\ 1$
$\bar{1}\ 1\ 1$	five	$1\ \bar{1}\ \bar{1}$
$\bar{1}\ 1\ 0$	six	$1\ \bar{1}\ 0$
$\bar{1}\ 1\ \bar{1}$	seven	$1\ \bar{1}\ 1$
$\bar{1}\ 0\ 1$	eight	$1\ 0\ \bar{1}$
$\bar{1}\ 0\ 0$	nine	$1\ 0\ 0$
$\bar{1}\ 0\ \bar{1}$	ten	$1\ 0\ 1$

The great advantage of such a balanced notation is that it eliminates the distinction between positive and negative numbers. Changing the sign of a number, or complementing, is accomplished by simply changing $\bar{1}$ to 1 and 1 to $\bar{1}$, digit by digit.

The addition and multiplication tables and the rules of signs may be combined as follows:

Addition

+	$\bar{1}$	0	1
$\bar{1}$	$\bar{1}1$	$\bar{1}$	0
0	$\bar{1}$	0	1
1	0	1	$1\bar{1}$

Multiplication

×	$\bar{1}$	0	1
$\bar{1}$	1	0	$\bar{1}$
0	0	0	0
1	$\bar{1}$	0	1

Another proposal seeks to eliminate not only the distinction between positive and negative numbers but also between real and complex numbers.[5] It has been called the "quater-imaginary" system and uses the imaginary number $2i$ as its base.[6] The numerals used in this system are 0, 1, 2, and 3. A typical number in this system might be $(321.2)_{2i}$ which represents the sum

$$3 \times (2i)^2 + 2 \times (2i)^1 + 1 \times (2i)^0 + 2 \times (2i)^{-1}$$

or

[5] Knuth, Donald E.: "An Imaginary Number System," *Comm. Assoc. Comp. Mach.* (3), No. 4, pp. 245–247, April 1960.

[6] Recall that $2i$ is that number whose square is -4, i. e., $(2i)^2 = -4$ or $2i = \sqrt{-4}$.

$$3 \times (-4) + 4i + 1 + (-i) = (-11 + 3i)_{10}.$$

Similarly, "plus one" is represented by 1, "minus one" by 103, "plus i" by 10.2, and "minus i" by 0.2.

The addition and multiplication tables for this system appear as follows:

Addition

+	0	1	2	3
0	0	1	2	3
1	1	2	3	10300
2	2	3	10300	10301
3	3	10300	10301	10302

Multiplication

×	0	1	2	3
0	0	0	0	0
1	0	1	2	3
2	0	2	10300	10302
3	0	3	10302	10201

Some thought has also been given to a so-called "residue number system" in which the operations of addition, subtraction, and multiplication may be executed in the same period of time without the need for carrying.[7]

Thus the computer has encouraged much thinking about number systems. It has led to the use of number systems which are attractive to the computer designer in terms of simplified circuitry and speed of execution. Even more important than this, however, is the possible value of these new systems in other branches of mathematics—in proving theorems, in making generalizations, and in unifying some of our concepts.

Exercises

1. Convert each of the following to the decimal system: (a) $(10111101)_2$, (b) $(67305)_8$, (c) $(44023)_5$, (d) $(20122)_3$.

2. Convert each of the following to the decimal system: (a) $(110111)_{-2}$, (b) $(10.011)_{-2}$, (c) $(203.13)_{2i}$.

3. Perform the indicated operations in the binary system.

(a) $\begin{array}{r} 10111 \\ +\ 1111 \\ \hline \end{array}$ (b) $\begin{array}{r} 11011 \\ -\ 1101 \\ \hline \end{array}$ (c) $\begin{array}{r} 110111 \\ \times\ \ 101 \\ \hline \end{array}$

[7] Garner, Harvey L.: "The Residue Number System," *IRE Trans. on Elec. Comp.* (EC-8), No. 2, pp. 140–147, June 1959.

4. Perform the indicated operations in the octal system. (a) 7654 + 6307, (b) 7213 − 567, (c) 346 × 47, (d) 4771 ÷ 105.
5. What operation will change the binary number 101.11 to 1011.1?
6. Convert the following numbers written in the decimal system to their binary equivalents: (a) 386, (b) 7.8, (c) 89, (d) 30.5, (e) 1964.
7. Perform the indicated operations in the balanced ternary system:
   (a) $\bar{1}1\bar{1} + 101$, (b) $\bar{1}11 \times 1\bar{1}\bar{1}$,
   (c) $100 - \bar{1}01$, (d) $\bar{1}0\bar{1} \div 1\bar{1}\bar{1}$.
8. Find the ten's complement of (a) 186, (b) 3839, (c) 60789.
9. Find the minus-one complement of the binary numbers:(a) 10111, (b) 110010, (c) 11.01101, (d) .0011.
10. Convert $-5 + 2i$ to the quater-imaginary system.
11. Show that the number 0.111 · · · expressed in Bergman's irrational base is greater than "one" in the decimal system.
12. Show that in Bergman's irrational number system a number may have infinitely many representations. (Hint: consider .110000 and .1011000).

3. Getting Started with a Guess

A characteristic of digital computers that usually perplexes the beginner is the fact that it is not possible to work with indeterminate quantities. In algebra we work with indeterminate quantities almost exclusively. The letter x in the polynomial equation

$$x^2 + 2x - 6 = 0$$

is an indeterminate. We determine the values of x that satisfy the equation by a procedure in which we don't need to know what x is. In fact, we usually do not know until the last step. Then we use the numerical values of x we obtain in checking that these are actually the correct values.

In a digital computer, however, we cannot carry along such an indeterminate but must assign some numerical value to it. Unless we're psychic this assigned number will not be the correct one. By using the proper algorithm[1] we can correct the number

[1] An algorithm is a computational scheme. Long-division, extracting square roots, finding the roots of a quadratic equation, etc., are usually done by means of appropriate algorithms.

systematically so that it approaches nearer the true value. This is the basis of a large number of calculations which are performed on the digital computer.

Naturally, we don't want to do any more work than absolutely necessary, nor do we want the computer to run unnecessarily. Computers are expensive and even though the arithmetic operations can be performed in millionths of a second, care must be exercised. It is very easy to let a complex problem get so out of hand that it runs for several hours on the computer.

Hence our starting values or initial guesses must be as close to the truth as possible. The importance of a good starting guess can be illustrated by means of an example.

Suppose we wish to find $\sqrt{N}$. We consider the equation

$$x^2 - N = 0$$

and seek to find its positive root. If we let x_0 be an initial guess (sometimes more or less facetiously called the zeroth approximation) then the exact value can be represented by $x_0 + h$. In other words, $x_0 + h$ satisfies the original equation; that is,

$$(x_0 + h)^2 - N = x_0^2 + 2x_0h + h^2 - N = 0 .$$

Since h is the correction factor that must be applied to x_0, our task is accomplished if we can determine h.

Unfortunately, the last equation is as difficult to solve for h as the original was for x. However, we can now make some reasonable simplifications. *If x_0 is a good approximation* to N, then h is necessarily small (certainly less than 1) and h^2 is much smaller still. Thus we can discard the h^2 term in the last equation to obtain

$$x_0^2 + 2x_0h - N = 0 .$$

This is now easily solved for h and we have

$$h = \frac{N - x_0^2}{2x_0} .$$

We may call this the initial correction, h_0, and define the next approximation x_1 as[2]

$$x_1 = x_0 + h_0 = \frac{N + x_0^2}{2x_0}. \tag{3.1}$$

As a numerical example, suppose we take $N = 42$ and an initial guess for $\sqrt{42}$ as 6. Then

$$x_1 = \frac{42 + 36}{2(6)} = 6.5$$

$$x_2 = \frac{N + x_1^2}{2x_1} = \frac{42 + 42.25}{2(6.5)} = 6.48\,.$$

As a check, we find that $(6.48)^2 = 41.99$ so that we obtained a good answer with very little labor.

Now suppose our initial guess had been wild, say 3. Then

$$x_1 = \frac{42 + 9}{2(3)} = 8.5$$

$$x_2 = \frac{42 + 72.25}{2(8.5)} = 6.72$$

$$x_3 = \frac{42 + 45.16}{2(6.72)} = 6.49\,.$$

Again as a check we find that $(6.49)^2 = 42.12$ which is not nearly as close as before. Moreover the labor was increased by approximately 50 per cent.

Now it turns out that making a close guess to the solution of a problem is not restricted to problems solved with computers. It is a general procedure that should constantly be applied because it is good mathematics. It produces a frame of mind which can more easily cope with the most difficult problems. The guessed solution also provides an excellent check on the reasonableness of the solution when it is finally obtained. Finally, a good first guess will save time and effort and lead one to solu-

[2] This is known as the Newton (or Newton-Raphson) formula; we shall meet it again in a later chapter.

tions of problems that are particularly difficult. Let us look at some results of good guessing.

First, in a scheme for finding the square root of a number, we have already seen how important it is to have a good starting value. If we wish to find $\sqrt{N}$ and $1 \leq N \leq 100$, then it turns out that a good starting value is given by

$$x_0 = 2 + N/10.$$

Another scheme, not quite as simple as the last one, is one which can be used with any number greater than 1. Count the number of digits in the number N whose square root is desired. Suppose N has n digits. Then $2(\sqrt{10})^{n-1}$ can be used as a starting value for $\sqrt{N}$. This kind of estimating produces a number that is known as a "ball-park number." Under these conditions it is entirely appropriate to use 3.2 for $\sqrt{10}$.

It can be readily appreciated that the matter of obtaining good first estimates is a highly individual one and depends collectively on a person's knowledge and ingenuity, and on the nature of the problem.

Exercises

1. Use the Newton-Raphson algorithm to find $\sqrt{495}$ correct to two decimal places.
2. Repeat exercise 1 using a starting guess of 10.
3. Devise a scheme for obtaining a starting value when the problem is to find the cube root of a number N.
4. Find $\sqrt{.0275}$ correct to 3 decimal places.

4. Interpolation, or Filling in the Gaps

One characteristic of a graph such as the one shown below is that it is *connected* for $a < x < b$. This means that, at least theoretically, we can read off the y-value corresponding to any of the infinite x-values between a and b (Figure 2).

If we had to represent such a quantity y in a digital com-

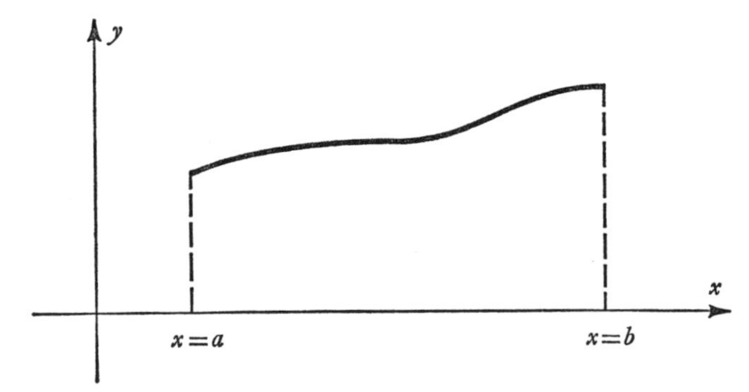

Fig. 2. A connected graph.

puter, we could do it only by considering a *finite* set of pairs (x, y). In other words, we would have to decide *which* values of x we wanted to use and then match the proper y-values to these. Thus, instead of a continuous graph, we would have one with the appearance of Figure 3. Each point corresponds to a pair of values of x and y. A graph such as this one consisting of a finite number of points is said to be *discrete*, that is, separate or individually distinct.

This may seem to be a *simplification* of the continuous graph but difficulties arise when, in the course of computing, an x-value is obtained which does not correspond to one of the

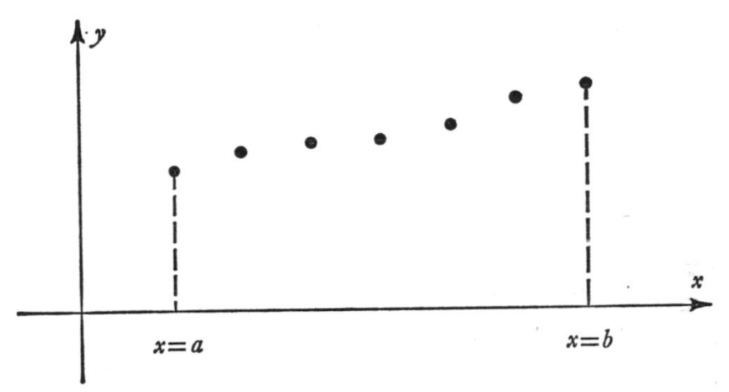

Fig. 3. A discrete graph.

given values. We must have some way of filling in the gaps between the x-values. This "filling in" is called *interpolation.*

We can find a number of examples of interpolation in our everyday lives. If we measure something with a ruler, we generally have to interpolate, that is, fill in between the graduations. The same thing applies to telling time, reading a thermometer, weighing oneself, etc. Almost invariably we use a form of interpolation that is called straight-line or *linear interpolation.* This is the simplest to use and is sufficiently accurate in the majority of cases.

Let us focus our attention on two points of the discrete graph. An enlarged view might look like Figure 4. By linear

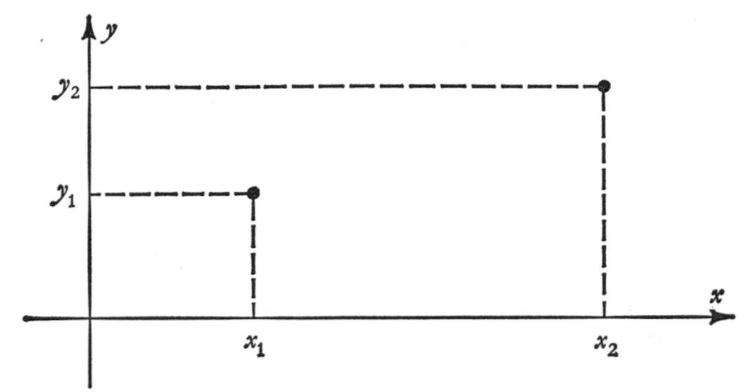

Fig. 4. Enlarged view of two points of Fig. 3.

interpolation we mean that if we had a value of x *halfway* between x_1 and x_2, we would take a corresponding y-value *halfway* between y_1 and y_2. If we were interested in an x-value *one-third* of the way from x_1 to x_2, we would take as the corresponding y-value *one-third* of the way from y_1 to y_2.

Linear interpolation is simply a matter of similar triangles. Enlarging our two points once again and adding an arbitrary point in between gives Figure 5. Now by considering the similar triangles we have

$$\frac{x_2 - x_1}{x - x_1} = \frac{y_2 - y_1}{y - y_1} \tag{4.1}$$

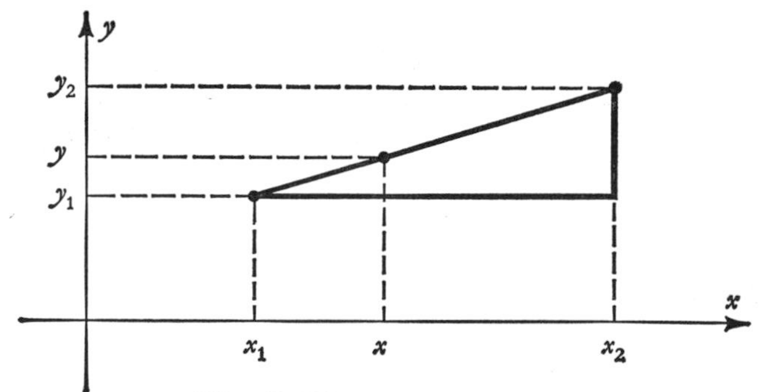

Fig. 5. Linear interpolation.

which, when solved for y, gives

$$y = y_1 + (x - x_1)\left(\frac{y_2 - y_1}{x_2 - x_1}\right).$$

If we are interested in the value of x, given the y-value, we solve equation (4.1) for x to get

$$x = \frac{x_1y_2 - x_2y_1}{y_2 - y_1} + y\left(\frac{x_2 - x_1}{y_2 - y_1}\right). \tag{4.2}$$

It should be apparent that assuming a straight line between two points of our discrete graph cannot result in too much error as long as the points are close together. For this reason, we ordinarily employ linear interpolation when we use trigonometric tables or tables of logarithms. The spacing in these tables is usually small and the entries in the table seldom go beyond five decimals.

If greater precision is essential and we have tables of values to, say, ten decimals, then linear interpolation is no longer sufficiently accurate. This is the situation facing the computer programmer. The computer is capable of operating on numbers having a large number of decimal places. It would not be very intelligent to use methods which did not take advantage of this capability.

There are many choices available to us if we decide *not* to use linear interpolation. For example, we could fit a parabola[1] between the two points instead of a straight line. The resulting interpolation would then be *quadratic interpolation.* We could also use a polynomial equation of the third degree leading to *cubic interpolation.* The whole process can be generalized to n-th degree polynomials and a good assortment of these are available.

There are also special methods which give better results than linear interpolation. Suppose we wish to find log π. To

[1] A parabola is the graph of the polynomial equation of the second degree: $y = ax^2 + bx + c$, where a, b, and c are arbitrary constants, with $a \neq 0$.

ten decimal places this is known to be[2] 0.49714 98727. If we use a 10-place table we can obtain

$$\log 3.14 = 0.49692\ 96481$$

and

$$\log 3.15 = 0.49831\ 05538\,.$$

The difference of these two is

$$\Delta = 0.00138\ 09057\,.$$

Now calculate the number S as follows:

$$S = \frac{\pi - 3.14}{3.15 - 3.14} = 0.15926\ 536\,.$$

Then

$$\Delta \times S = 0.00021\ 99304 \tag{4.3}$$

and

$$\frac{3.15}{\pi} \times \Delta \times S = 0.00022\ 05190\,. \tag{4.4}$$

The sum of these last two is 0.00044 04494.
Dividing this by two and adding to log 3.14 gives

$$\begin{array}{r} 0.00022\ 02247 \\ +0.49692\ 96481 \\ \hline 0.49714\ 98728 \end{array}$$

This agrees with the actual value of log π in all but the last place. Using linear interpolation we would have obtained a value which agreed with the correct one in only the first 6 places.

This example shows the ingenuity a mathematician must use in order to attain his purpose. The above scheme is due to the Hungarian mathematician Géza Huszár.[3]

[2] When working with numbers containing many decimal places, it is convenient to write the digits in groups of five.

[3] Huszár, Géza: "Egy Új Interpolációs Módszerről" (On a New Method

The above interpolation scheme may seem like black magic to the reader who has never thought about anything except linear interpolation. We may get some idea of Huszár's method by looking at an enlarged diagram. Using analytic geometry, let the coordinates of the points P_1 P_2 and P_3 be given by $P_1(x_1, y_1)$, $P_2(x_2, y_2)$, $P_3(x_3, y_3)$ (Figure 6).

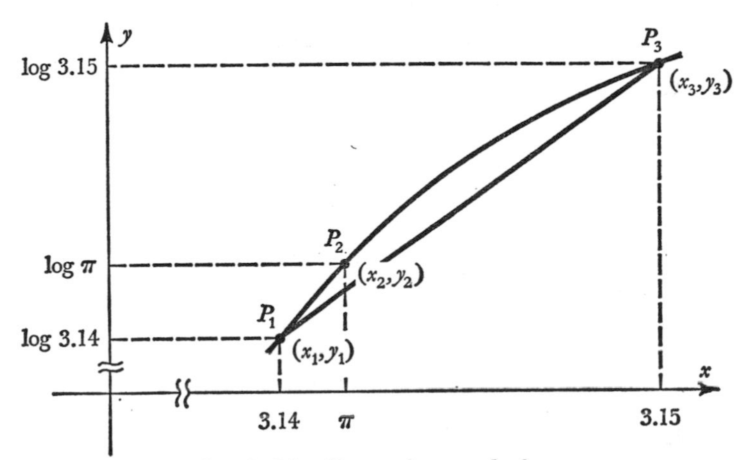

Fig. 6. Nonlinear interpolation.

The slope of the line $\overline{P_1P_3}$ is given by

$$\frac{y_3 - y_1}{x_3 - x_1},$$

hence any point (x, y) on the line $\overline{P_1P_3}$ satisfies the equation

$$y - y_1 = \frac{y_3 - y_1}{x_3 - x_1}(x - x_1) . \tag{4.5}$$

To a *first* approximation the point (x_2, y_2) can be considered to lie on the line whose equation is given by (4.5). In other words $x = \pi, y = \log \pi$ satisfy (4.5) so that we have

$$\log \pi - \log 3.14 = \frac{\log 3.15 - \log 3.14}{3.15 - 3.14}(\pi - 3.14) .$$

of Interpolation) in Hungarian. Transactions of the First Hungarian Mathematical Congress, Aug. 27–Sept. 2, 1950, pp. 727–730. Published by Akadémiai Kiadó, Budapest, 1952.

But the right side of this equation is the same as (4.3). Thus the *vertical* distance between P_1 and P_2 of Figure 6 is given by (4.3).

If P_2 is considered to lie on the line $\overline{P_1P_3}$, then we can see that (4.3) will give a result which is too small. According to Huszár's paper,[4] if (4.3) is multiplied by $3.15/\pi$ (which is slightly more than one) then (4.4) will result which is too large. He then takes the arithmetic average of the values in (4.3) and (4.4) and calls this that which must be added to log 3.14 to get log π.

This example is given so that the reader will have some idea of the great possibilities that exist in computer-type mathematics. We hesitate to give the simplest examples or the most difficult ones but must content ourselves with conveying the spirit of this type of mathematics as best we can.

Exercises

1. Why does it make more sense to interpolate linearly in a three-place table of logarithms than in a six-place table? Doesn't this violate your understanding of interpolation? Explain.
2. What characteristics of digital computers make linear interpolation undesirable?
3. Given log 3.14123 19059 862 = 0.4971 and log 3.14195 52846 411 = 0.4972, find log π($\pi \doteq$ 3.14159 26535 898)[5] by using equation (4.3).
4. Solve exercise 3 by using linear interpolation.
5. Why is linear interpolation desirable when telling time and getting weighed on the bathroom scales?

[4] The details are too technical for our purposes here and on this point we must rely on intuition.

[5] The symbol $\doteq$ is read "approximately equal to."

5. Approximations, Plain and Fancy

It is a fact of mathematical life that computations can seldom be carried out in a way that produces precise results. This is especially true when working with digital computers. We cannot even represent the number $\frac{1}{3}$, for example, in a digital computer but must settle for an approximation. Whether we instruct the machine to divide 1 by 3 or set the counter directly, we get the same result—a row of threes that must necessarily stop. We have also seen that a continuous graph must be approximated by a finite number of points.

This may appear to be an undesirable limitation of the digital computer but we will see that approximations of various kinds serve to open up new vistas in mathematics. From a practical standpoint it is approximation that enables us to use the computer's fifth-grade arithmetic ability to solve complicated problems. In fact the *modus operandi* is quite often as follows:

1) guess a number
2) use this guess to obtain an approximate solution
3) refine or correct this solution as many times as necessary.

The first step in the above process has already been discussed in Chapter 3, and we will also have occasion to talk about it later. The present chapter is concerned with the second step, while the third step—called iteration—will be discussed in Chapter 6.

As a point of departure, let us consider again the problem of finding the square root of a number N. Assume that by some means we have arrived at x_n, the nth approximation to $\sqrt{N}$. We would like the next approximation x_{n+1} to be nearer $\sqrt{N}$.

In other words, assuming that $(x_n - \sqrt{N})$ is small, how can we insure that $(x_{n+1} - \sqrt{N})$ will be smaller? If by "small" we mean a number between 0 and 1, then the *square* of such a number will be smaller. Thus we can set $(x_{n+1} - \sqrt{N})$ equal to some (as yet) unknown quantity k times $(x_n - \sqrt{N})^2$. This gives

$$\begin{aligned} x_{n+1} - \sqrt{N} &= k(x_n - \sqrt{N})^2 \\ &= kx_n^2 - 2kx_n\sqrt{N} + kN \\ &= k(x_n^2 + N) - 2kx_n\sqrt{N}. \end{aligned} \tag{5.1}$$

Now the only way to eliminate the unknown, $\sqrt{N}$, from the last equation is to have

$$2kx_n = 1$$

$$k = \frac{1}{2x_n}.$$

In this case equation (5.1) becomes

$$x_{n+1} = \frac{1}{2x_n}(x_n^2 + N)$$

or

$$x_{n+1} = \frac{1}{2}\left(x_n + \frac{N}{x_n}\right). \tag{5.2}$$

We can then begin the computation of $\sqrt{N}$ by setting $n = 0$ in (5.2), and providing a value x_0. We then obtain a value x_1 which is generally closer to $\sqrt{N}$ than x_0 was. We can actually predict how much closer x_1 is because if x_0 was in error by 0.1, the operation of squaring will reduce the error in x_1 to $(0.1)^2$ or 0.01. A process like this that doubles the number of significant figures at each stage is called a *second order process.*

Equation (5.2) has been met before in Chapter 3. It appeared there as equation (3.1) and was obtained by a slightly different method—one that Newton probably used originally.

The question naturally arises whether the above method can be used to develop other useful approximations. As another example,[1] suppose we wish to approximate the reciprocal of a number, a. In other words, we wish to find an expression x_n which is nearly $1/a$. We can minimize the difference between these two,

$$1/a - x_n$$

by minimizing

$$1 - ax_n \, .$$

Proceeding as before, to insure that $(1 - ax_{n+1})$ will be smaller than $(1 - ax_n)$, we set

$$\begin{aligned} 1 - ax_{n+1} &= k(1 - ax_n)^2 \\ &= k - 2akx_n + a^2kx_n^2 \, . \end{aligned}$$

We can easily solve this last equation for x_{n+1} if $k = 1$. Then

$$-ax_{n+1} = -2ax_n + a^2x_n^2$$

or

$$x_{n+1} = x_n(2 - ax_n) \, . \tag{5.3}$$

This is again a second-order process which can be demonstrated by taking a numerical example. Suppose $a = 3$, and we wish to use equation (5.3) to find $\frac{1}{3}$. Starting with an initial guess of $x_0 = 0.3$, the successive steps in the computation appear

[1] Cundy, H. M.: "Reciprocals by Iteration," *Math. Gazette* (45), no. 354, p. 333, December 1961.

as follows:

$$x_1 = 0.3\,[2 - 3(0.3)] = 0.33$$
$$x_2 = 0.33\,[2 - 3(0.33)] = 0.3333$$
$$x_3 = 0.3333\,[2 - 3(0.3333)] = 0.33333333$$

etc.

Here we can easily see the characteristic of a second-order process, namely, the number of significant figures is doubled at each step.

Someone may very well ask why we even consider an approximation such as contained in equation (5.3) rather than obtaining the reciprocal by division. We hasten to point out that the above method employs the operations of multiplication and subtraction just as a division process does. The advantage of this type of approximation formula is that on some kinds of computers (including some desk calculators) it is more convenient to multiply than to divide. Moreover, from a purely academic standpoint it is intriguing to demonstrate that multiplication and division *are* inverse processes so that it is possible to divide by multiplying.

Many forms of approximation owe their origin to an old method of finding roots of polynomial equations. This method, known as *regula falsi* or "the method of false position" was known to the Egyptians between 1850 and 1650 B.C. Suppose we wish to find a real root of the polynomial equation $f(x) = 0$ and suppose the graph of this equation (if we knew it exactly) appears as in Figure 7.

The problem here is to find the value of x, say $x = r$, at which the graph crosses the x-axis. If $f(x)$ is a continuous function and we can locate two points a and b such that $f(a)$ and $f(b)$ are opposite in sign, then it is evident that the graph crosses the x-axis at some point between a and b. That is, $a < r < b$. As a first approximation, consider the point x_0 where the chord joining the points A and B of the graph crosses the x-axis. This point x_0 is the "false position" of the point r.

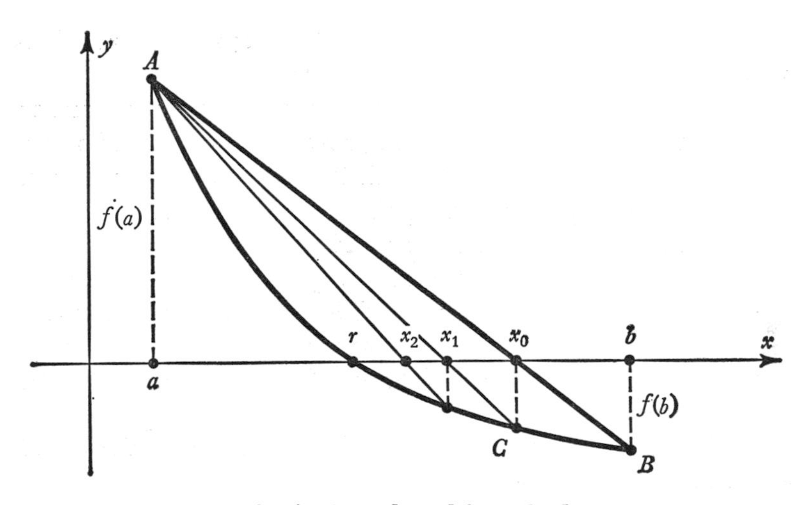

Fig. 7. *Regula falsi* method.

Since we know the coordinates of the points A and B, namely, $[a, f(a)]$ and $[b, f(b)]$ respectively, we can write the equation of the chord AB. We have

$$y - f(a) = \frac{f(b) - f(a)}{b - a} (x - a) . \qquad (5.4)$$

Our interest is in the value of x when y is zero. Solving for x after putting $y = 0$, gives

$$x = x_0 = a + \frac{f(a)}{f(a) - f(b)} (b - a) . \qquad (5.5)$$

Now since $f(a)$ and $f(b)$ are of opposite sign and $a < x_0 < b$, it follows that $f(x_0)$ must be opposite in sign to one of $f(a)$ or $f(b)$. In the above figure $f(x_0)$ is opposite in sign to $f(a)$. Hence we can repeat the previous process with x_0 now playing the role of b and obtain a new approximation from (5.5) by analogy,

$$x_1 = a + \frac{f(a)}{f(a) - f(x_0)} (x_0 - a) . \qquad (5.6)$$

This process can be continued until a value x_{k+1} is obtained which differs insignificantly from the previous value x_k. This x_k is then an approximate value of the root r.

It should be mentioned that the method of false position gives best results when used to improve the accuracy of a root once it is known approximately. This is due to the fact that as the successive approximating points get closer and closer together, the graph becomes more nearly a straight line.

The method of false position is quite simple in principle, replacing as it does the graph of $f(x)$ between any two points a and b by its chord. Thus it is an example of inverse linear interpolation, and equations (5.5) and (5.6) express those values of x for which $f(x) = 0$.

We call attention to the fact that the slope of the chord AB in the last figure is[2]

$$m_{AB} = \frac{f(a) - f(b)}{a - b}.$$

Hence equation (5.5) can also be written as

$$x_0 = a - \frac{f(a)}{m_{AB}},$$

and (5.6) can be written as

$$x_1 = a - \frac{f(a)}{m_{AC}}. \qquad (5.7)$$

Sir Isaac Newton's contribution consisted of replacing the slope of the *chord* by the slope of the *curve*.[3] For example, instead of using m_{AC}, the slope of the chord AC, in equation (5.7), Newton used the slope of the curve *at the point* x_1. The value of this slope depends not only on the point x_1 but also on the particular function under consideration. Hence it is customary to use the notation $f'(x_1)$ to represent the value of the slope of the function $f(x)$ at the point where x is x_1.

[2] m_{AB} is the symbol for "the slope of the line joining the points A and B."

[3] By the slope of a curve at a given point we mean the slope of the *tangent to the curve* at that point.

In the calculus $f'(x_1)$ is also called "the derivative of $f(x)$ with respect to x evaluated at $x = x_1$." One of the objectives in calculus is to find the derivatives of various functions. The branch of calculus called *differential calculus* is concerned with this problem and a number of formulas are derived so that one can find the derivatives of quite complicated functions.

The Newton formula for the approximate root of the equation $f(x) = 0$ is given by

$$x_{n+1} = x_n - \frac{f(x_n)}{f'(x_n)}, \tag{5.8}$$

which shows how to improve a root x_n previously obtained. The meaning of this formula can best be obtained geometrically. In the following figure we consider x_n to be an approximation to the root r of the equation $f(x) = 0$. Then the value x_{n+1} represents the point at which the tangent to the curve at $x = x_n$ crosses the x-axis (Figure 8).

Formula (5.8) has wide applicability and can be used with many continuous functions. If the function doesn't change sign,

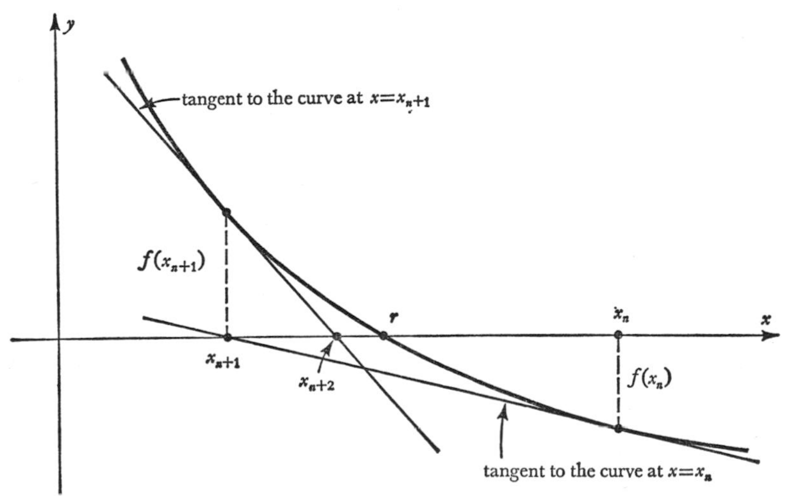

Fig. 8. Newton's method.

however, it doesn't have any *real* zeros and neither Newton's method nor the method of false position is applicable.

We can now use Newton's formula to obtain approximate values of various functions in ways which are especially suited to computers. As a variation of the square root problem, suppose we wish to find the reciprocal square root of a number N, i.e., $1/\sqrt{N}$.

Consider the equation

$$f(x) = N - 1/x^2 = 0\,,$$

whose root x is the desired quantity. It is known from the differential calculus that

$$f'(x) = 2/x^3$$

hence

$$f'(x_n) = 2/x_n^3 \quad \text{and} \quad f(x_n) = N - 1/x_n^2\,.$$

Substituting these values into equation (5.8) we obtain

$$x_{n+1} = \frac{x_n}{2}(3 - Nx_n^2)\,.$$

We can rewrite this as

$$x_{n+1} = 0.5x_n(3 - Nx_n^2) \tag{5.9}$$

and obtain a formula for the reciprocal square root which is ideally adapted to computers because it requires no divisions. Even more remarkable is the fact that one more multiplication can convert this formula to one for finding square root without divisions. Having found

$$x = 1/\sqrt{N}\,,$$

multiplication of both members by N produces

$$\sqrt{N} = Nx\,.$$

As an example of the use of formula (5.9), suppose we wish to find $\sqrt{2}$. We first find $1/\sqrt{2}$, using (5.9) with $N = 2$ and, say, $x_0 = \frac{1}{2}$. Then we obtain

$$x_1 = 0.5(0.5)\,[3 - 2(0.5)^2] = 0.625$$

$$x_2 = 0.5(0.625)\,[3 - 2(0.625)^2] = 0.6934$$

$$x_3 = 0.5(0.6934)\,[3 - 2(0.6934)^2] = 0.70671\,.$$

Multiplying this last by N, that is 2, gives[4]

$$\sqrt{2} \doteq 1.41342\,,$$

compared to the actual 1.41421.

We conclude this chapter by giving some unusual approximations in order to show that there is almost no limit to the mathematician's flights of imagination.

First, we give an ancient method for approximating the nth root of a rational number. This method is due to Diophantus of Alexandria, celebrated for his writings on algebra, who lived about 300 A.D.

Diophantus proceeded in the following manner: To find the nth root of a rational number such as r/s, first write it in the form p/q^n by multiplying numerator and denominator by the necessary integer to make the denominator a perfect nth power. Then multiply p by the nth powers of successive integers until pa^n is sufficiently close to a perfect nth power, say b^n. The required approximation is then b/aq.

As an illustration of the method of Diophantus, suppose we seek $\sqrt[3]{\frac{2}{3}}$. We write

$$\frac{2}{3} = \frac{18}{27} = \frac{18}{3^3}\,.$$

Next we multiply 18 by the cubes of successive integers.[5] This can be arranged in a table as follows:

$$18\cdot 1^3 = 18 \times 1 = 18$$

$$18\cdot 2^3 = 18 \times 8 = 144$$

[4] The symbol $\doteq$ is read "is approximately equal to."

[5] A table of cubes is convenient for this work. Such tables were available to Diophantus.

$$18 \cdot 3^3 = 18 \times 27 = 486$$
$$18 \cdot 4^3 = 18 \times 64 = 1152$$
$$18 \cdot 5^3 = 18 \times 125 = 2250$$
$$18 \cdot 6^3 = 18 \times 216 = 3888$$
$$18 \cdot 7^3 = 18 \times 343 = 6174$$
$$18 \cdot 8^3 = 18 \times 512 = 9216.$$

Now 9216 is close to 9261 which is 21^3. Hence the required approximation is given by

$$\sqrt[3]{\tfrac{2}{3}} \doteq \frac{21}{8 \times 3} = 0.875\,,$$

which compares favorably with the actual 0.873.

Another method which can be easily adapted to computers was developed by Hero of Alexandria over two thousand years ago. This is again a method for finding square roots.

Consider the number 29,929 whose square root we seek. If we "guess" 173 and divide 29,929 by 173 we obtain 173. That is,

$$29{,}929 \div 173 = 173\,.$$

This clearly establishes that 173 is the correct solution.

Lacking occult powers, however, we would be more inclined to use 170 as a first guess. Then the division

$$29{,}929 \div 170 \doteq 176$$

indicates that 170 is too small and that 176 is too large. It is quite natural to take for the next trial the arithmetic average of 170 and 176. Another division then establishes the accuracy of this value.

One advantage of this method is that its successive steps are all similar and that any desired accuracy can be obtained. For example, to find $\sqrt{56}$ with a first guess of 7, the work proceeds as follows:

$$56 \div 7 = 8 \qquad \frac{8+7}{2} = 7.5$$

$$56 \div 7.5 = 7.47 \qquad \frac{7.47 + 7.5}{2} = 7.485$$

$$56 \div 7.485 = 7.4816 \qquad \frac{7.485 + 7.4816}{2} = 7.4833$$

$$56 \div 7.4833. \quad \text{etc.}$$

Another advantage of this method is that it can be generalized to finding the nth root of any positive number N.[6] We write

$$N = x^n = x_1^{n-1} \times x_2$$

where x is the value sought, x_1 is an approximation to x, and x_2 is found by dividing N by x_1^{n-1}. The next approximation x_3 is found by taking the *weighted* average of x_1 and x_2, that is,

$$x_3 = \frac{(n-1)x_1 + 1 \times x_2}{n}. \qquad (5.10)$$

Having obtained x_3, we write

$$N = x_3^{n-1} \times x_4$$

where x_4 is obtained by dividing N by x_3^{n-1}. We proceed in like manner until the desired accuracy is reached.

The steps for finding $\sqrt[3]{56}$ follow:

$$N = 56, \quad n = 3, \quad \text{take } x_1 = 4$$

$$x_2 = \frac{56}{4^2} = 3.5 \qquad x_3 = \frac{2(4) + 3.5}{3} = 3.83$$

$$x_4 = \frac{56}{(3.83)^2} = 3.8176 \qquad x_5 = \frac{2(3.83) + 3.8176}{3} = 3.8259$$

$$x_6 = \frac{56}{(3.8259)^2} = 3.8258.$$

This compares favorably with the actual 3.82586.

[6] Ballantine, J. P.: "An Averaging Method of Extracting Roots," *Amer. Math. Monthly* (63), no. 4, pp. 249–252, April 1956.

Approximations, Plain and Fancy

Cecil Hastings[7] has developed some rather unusual approximations by methods all his own. For example, he gives

$$\sqrt{x} \doteq \frac{1 + 4x}{4 + x}$$

which is in error by less than one part in 12 provided that

$$0.1 \leq x \leq 10 .$$

He also gives

$$\log x \doteq -0.076 + 0.281x - 0.238/(x + 0.15)$$

which has an error less than 0.005 for all x satisfying

$$0.1 \leq x \leq 1 .$$

Thus we have many ways to approximate functions in mathematics. Some of these are old, some new, and others are adaptations of old methods. The point is that though there is already quite a variety, there are many more still to be discovered.

Exercises

1. Find $\sqrt{3}$ correct to three decimals by two methods described in this chapter.
2. Find the reciprocal of 3.5 correct to ten decimals.
3. Given the polynomial equation
$$y = x^3 - 3x^2 - 8x + 10 .$$
Find its smallest positive root.
(Hint: If $f(x) = x^3 - 3x^2 - 8x + 10$, then $f'(x) = 3x^2 - 6x - 8$).
4. Find $\sqrt{5}$ by finding the reciprocal square root. Use as good a first guess as possible.
5. Do exercise 4 again but this time change your initial guess by a factor of 2 or 3. How does the work compare with that in exercise 4?
6. Find $\sqrt[4]{\frac{3}{4}}$ by Diophantus' method. Can you estimate the error?

[7] Hastings, Cecil: "Analytical Approximations," MTAC (VII), no. 41, pp. 67–69, January 1953.

7. Evaluate $\sqrt{3291}$ by the method of averages.
8. Evaluate $\sqrt[3]{736}$ by the method of weighted averages.
9. Use the method of Hastings to find $\sqrt{5}$. Compare the result with the answer to exercise 4.
10. Use Hastings' method to find log 0.5 and compare with that found in a table of logarithms.

6. Iteration: Repetition with a Purpose

The most useful feature of a digital computer is its great speed. Some planning is required, however, in order to take full advantage of this speed. Part of this planning has to do with having a good first guess at the start. Another part has to do with arranging the computation so that there is a lot of repetition.

Repetition of computations not only makes it easier to write instructions for a computer, but also makes the actual operation of the computer more efficient. We could not expect to take advantage of a fast production line in a factory if we gave different orders for the manufacture of each item. As soon as we ask for *duplicate* items, things hum along merrily.

Some of the techniques we have discussed in the last chapter are known as iterative techniques. Iteration in the computing sense means more than repetition. It's true that we do repeat the steps in a computation as we did in the last example when we were evaluating $\sqrt[3]{56}$. The fact is, however, that generally each repetition or iteration uses different numbers and produces a more accurate result.

Thus the most powerful computing methods are algorithms based on iteration. We will discuss a number of these in this chapter and again show that the computer has widened the mathematician's horizon.

A simple example of iteration is given by the solution of a quadratic equation by this method. If we are looking for a root of the equation

$$x^2 + 5.4x - 12.3 = 0, \tag{6.1}$$

we can develop an iterative procedure by solving this equation for x. We have

$$x(x + 5.4) = 12.3$$

$$x = \frac{12.3}{x + 5.4}.$$

We have been told that it is useless to solve an equation for the indeterminate in terms of the indeterminate, but let us see what happens.

We rewrite the last equation as

$$x_{n+1} = \frac{12.3}{x_n + 5.4}, \tag{6.2}$$

and this form gives a clue to the method we will use. Setting $n = 0$, we begin by substituting a first guess x_0 on the right. We perform the computation to find x_1. If our first guess is exact, we would expect that x_1 will turn out to be the same as x_0. If not, we repeat the process, this time with x_1 on the right.

The successive steps of the computation would appear as follows:

Assume $x_0 = 2$.

$$x_1 = \frac{12.3}{2 + 5.4} = 1.66,$$

$$x_2 = \frac{12.3}{1.66 + 5.4} = 1.74,$$

$$x_3 = \frac{12.3}{1.74 + 5.4} = 1.70\,,$$

$$x_4 = \frac{12.3}{1.70 + 5.4} = 1.73\,,$$

$$x_5 = \frac{12.3}{1.73 + 5.4} = 1.725\,,$$

$$x_6 = \frac{12.3}{1.725 + 5.4} = 1.7263\,,$$

$$x_7 = \frac{12.3}{1.7263 + 5.4} = 1.7260\,.$$

At this point we would be safe in saying that a root is given by $x = 1.726$ correct to four significant figures. It should be apparent that we could continue the above process as long as desired.

Whether or not an iterative process such as this one can be used depends on the existence of a sequence of intermediate values $x_1, x_2, x_3, \cdots$, which tend to a limit. To clarify this

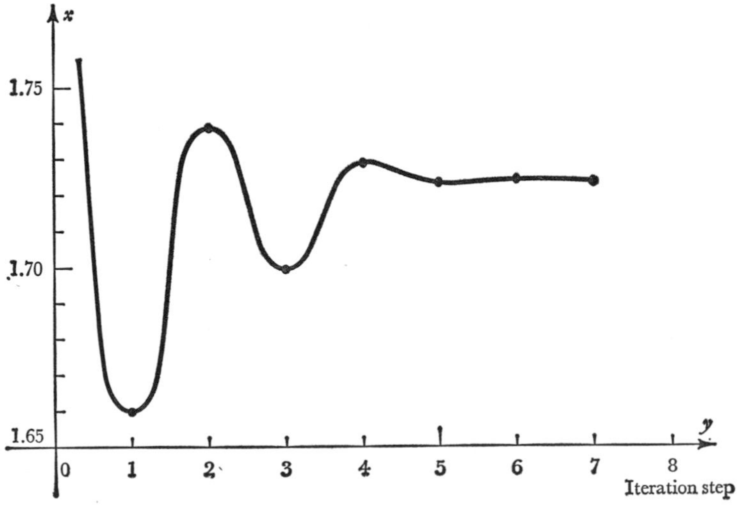

Fig. 9. Convergence of an iteration process.

idea we construct a graph which shows the values obtained in the last example (Figure 9).

Notice that in plotting x_5, x_6, and x_7 we could hardly indicate any difference in these values in spite of the fineness of the x-scale. It is characteristic of a sequence that converges that no matter how much we may magnify the scale, we will eventually reach a point where we can no longer distinguish between successive values.

A graph such as we made tells us not only to *what value* the sequence converges but also *how rapidly* it converges. At first the x-values oscillate considerably—x_1 being less than the "final" value, x_2 greater, x_3 less, etc. Then suddenly the oscillations become much less and we have convergence for all practical purposes. Behavior like this may be due to the fact that the algorithm being used converges rapidly if the starting guess is good. There is another reason, however, for this behavior, and if you are a careful reader, you may suspect the reason. We have deliberately introduced an error into our computations. The value of 1.70 given for x_3 is in error. Although this error affected all successive values, it did not prevent us from reaching a solution. This, of course, is an important advantage of the iterative method.

We should point out that we had to pay for the error we put into x_3 in terms of additional computing effort. The correct value of x_3 is 1.723 and this produces the values

$$x_4 = 1.727\,,$$

$$x_5 = 1.726\,.$$

Thus the error cost us two extra steps of computation.

There are, unfortunately, disadvantages to the iterative method also. Consider the quadratic equation

$$x^2 - 3.2x + 2.8 = 0\,. \qquad (6.3)$$

When put into the proper form for iteration this becomes

$$x_{n+1} = \frac{-2.8}{x_n - 3.2}\,.$$

The value $x_0 = 1$ appears to be a reasonable starting value and leads to

$$x_1 = \frac{-2.8}{1 - 3.2} = 1.27,$$

$$x_2 = \frac{-2.8}{1.27 - 3.2} = 1.45,$$

$$x_3 = \frac{-2.8}{1.45 - 3.2} = 1.60,$$

$$x_4 = \frac{-2.8}{1.60 - 3.2} = 1.75,$$

$$x_5 = \frac{-2.8}{1.75 - 3.2} = 1.93,$$

$$x_6 = \frac{-2.8}{1.93 - 3.2} = 2.20.$$

We would certainly tend to be discouraged even before we reached this point. A closer look at equation (6.3) reveals that the roots of this equation are complex numbers, hence we could not expect our iteration with its real initial guess to converge to a real number.

As another example, consider the quadratic equation

$$x^2 - 4.0x + 3.99 = 0. \qquad (6.4)$$

The discriminant[1] indicates that this equation has real roots so we put it into iterative form,

$$x_{n+1} = \frac{-3.99}{x_n - 4.0}.$$

Beginning with $x_0 = 2$, we have

$$x_1 = \frac{-3.99}{2 - 4.0} = 1.995,$$

[1] The discriminant of $ax^2 + bx + c = 0$ is $b^2 - 4ac$, and if it is not negative, the equation has real roots.

$$x_2 = \frac{-3.99}{1.995 - 4.0} = 1.990\,,$$

$$x_3 = \frac{-3.99}{1.990 - 4.0} = 1.985\,,$$

$$x_4 = \frac{-3.99}{1.985 - 4.0} = 1.980\,,$$

$$x_5 = \frac{-3.99}{1.980 - 4.0} = 1.975\,.$$

Again there is a strong tendency to be discouraged due to the apparent lack of convergence. This time, however, persistence would eventually lead us to the root 1.900. The great speed of the computer is a definite advantage in this case.

Fortunately, there is a criterion available for checking the rapidity of convergence of an iterative process. If the equation to be solved is $f(x) = 0$ and if this equation can be solved for x and written in the form

$$x = F(x) \tag{6.5}$$

then an iterative process applied to (6.5) will converge provided that

$$|F'(x)| < 1$$

in the neighborhood of the desired root.

Using some differential calculus and applying this criterion to equation (6.2), we find

$$F(x) = \frac{12.3}{x + 5.4}\,,$$

$$F'(x) = \frac{-12.3}{(x + 5.4)^2}\,,$$

$$F'(1.7) = \frac{-12.3}{(1.7 + 5.4)^2} = -0.24\,,$$

$$|F'(1.7)| = 0.24 < 1\,.$$

Of course it would have been more reasonable to check the rate of convergence by using the first guess, $x = 2$. Then

$$|F'(2)| = \left|\frac{-12.3}{(2 + 5.4)^2}\right| = 0.22 < 1 .$$

This again brings out the importance of having a good first guess.

Applying the convergence criterion to equation (6.4) gives

$$F(x) = \frac{-3.99}{x - 4.0},$$

$$F'(x) = \frac{3.99}{(x - 4.0)^2},$$

$$|F'(2)| = \frac{3.99}{(2 - 4.0)^2} = 0.9975 < 1 .$$

This time we are much closer to 1 than before and this is an indication of slow convergence. It can be shown that the smaller the absolute value of $F'(x)$ in the neighborhood of the desired root, the more rapid the convergence.

At this point one might very well ask if it is possible to speed up the rate of convergence of an iterative process. It would certainly be desirable to do so, especially if the process is being carried out without the use of a computer.

The order of an iteration formula indicates the rate of convergence of the iteration. Hence one way to speed up the rate of convergence is to develop an iterative procedure of higher order. Much of the present work in numerical analysis research is concerned with the development of such high-order processes.

We have already shown first and second order iterative methods for finding the square root of a number. Let us look at a third order process which was developed from Newton's formula.[2] Consider

[2] Jordan, William B.: "An Iterative Process", *MTAC* (V), no. 35, p. 183, July 1951.

$$x_{n+1} = \frac{x_n(x_n^2 + 3N)}{3x_n^2 + N}, \tag{6.7}$$

which is a third order process for computing $\sqrt{N}$. The very rapid rate of convergence can be demonstrated by an example. To find $\sqrt{10}$ with an initial guess of 3, we have

$$x_1 = \frac{3(9 + 30)}{3(9) + 10} = 3.16216\,,$$

$$x_2 = \frac{3.16216\,[(3.16216)^2 + 30]}{3(3.16216)^2 + 10} = 3.16227\ 76601\ 68341\,,$$

which is in error by 4 units in the last figure.

Another example of improving an iterative process is based on the method of finding the nth root of a positive number N discussed at the end of chapter 5. Recall that we wrote

$$N = x^n = x_1^{n-1} \times x_2$$

where x is the value sought, x_1 is an approximation to x, and x_2 is found by dividing N by x_1^{n-1}. The next approximation x_3 is found by taking the weighted average of x_1 and x_2. The usual practice is to give x_1 and x_2 weights $n - 1$ and 1, the same as their exponents in the above equation.

Better results are obtained, however, by making the weights depend on the values of x_1 and x_2. Ballantine[3] has shown that if the weights depend on x_1 and x_2 linearly, then in the case of square root,

$$\frac{(x_1 + 3x_2)x_1 + (3x_1 + x_2)x_2}{4(x_1 + x_2)}$$

produces a better result than taking the arithmetic average of x_1 and x_2. For cube root, he gives the formula

$$\frac{(5x_1 + 13x_2)x_1 + (7x_1 + 2x_2)x_2}{3(4x_1 + 5x_2)}$$

[3] Ballantine, J. P.: "An Averaging Method of Extracting Roots," *Amer. Math. Monthly* (63), no. 4. pp. 249–252, April 1956.

which is an improvement over

$$\frac{2x_1 + x_2}{3}.$$

In this way it is possible to develop a fourth order iterative process for the determination of an nth root.

Taking again the problem of finding $\sqrt[3]{56}$, we start as before,

$$N = 56, \quad n = 3, \quad \text{take } x_1 = 4$$

$$x_2 = \frac{56}{4^2} = 3.5.$$

Now instead of using weights 2 and 1 for x_1 and x_2, respectively, we take $(5x_1 + 13x_2)$ and $(7x_1 + 2x_2)$. In other words,

$$5x_1 + 13x_2 = 65.5,$$

and

$$7x_1 + 2x_2 = 35.0$$

become the new weights. The weighted average x_3 is now found to be

$$x_3 = \frac{65.5(4) + 35.0(3.5)}{65.5 + 35.0} = 3.82587.$$

This compares with the actual 3.82586 and the value 3.83 found in the previous chapter.

Earlier in this chapter we discussed an iterative method for obtaining the roots of a quadratic equation. This was really an artificial example because we have a perfectly good algorithm available—the quadratic formula. We are ready now to solve some problems by iteration for which *no* such convenient algorithm exists.

Suppose we wish to find a root of the equation

$$3x - \sqrt{1 + \sin x} = 0. \tag{6.8}$$

This is an example of a class of equations known as *transcendental*, that is, non-algebraic. There are no known general methods for determining the roots of such equations. Best results can be achieved when the work is performed in two stages. The first is a survey in which the general characteristics of the equation are investigated and in which the roots are located approximately. The second stage is a refinement, in which the roots are found to the desired degree of accuracy.

It should be noted that a transcendental equation may have a finite or an infinite number of roots, or it may have no real roots at all. For example, the equation

$$\sin x = 2$$

has no real roots but an infinity of complex roots; the equation

$$\sin x = \tfrac{1}{2}$$

has an infinite number of real roots; the equation

$$\sin x = \tfrac{1}{2}x$$

has three real roots.

Going back to equation (6.8) we make an approximate graph of the two components of (6.8), namely,

$$y_1 = 3x$$

and

$$y_2 = \sqrt{1 + \sin x}\,.$$

Figure 10 indicates that these two functions intersect at $x \doteq 0.4$ Then we solve (6.8) for x,

$$x = \tfrac{1}{3}\sqrt{1 + \sin x}\,,$$

from which we obtain an iteration formula

$$x_{n+1} = \tfrac{1}{3}\sqrt{1 + \sin x_n}\,.$$

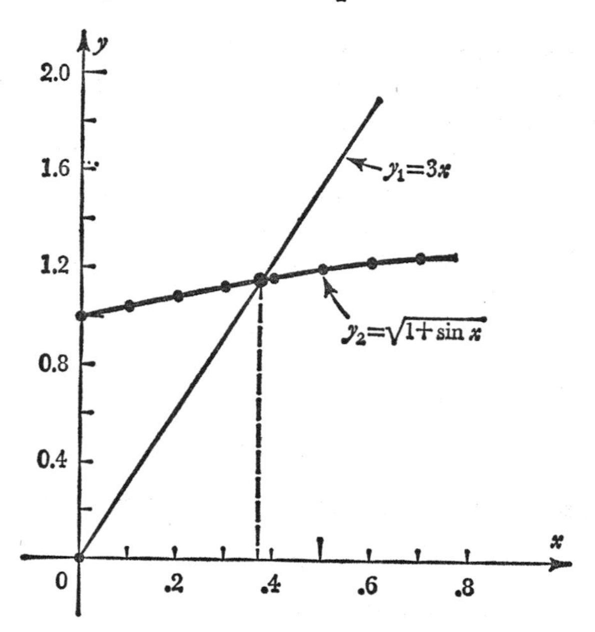

Fig. 10. Graphing to obtain an initial value.

We begin with $x_0 = 0.4$ and the computation yields[4]

$$x_1 = \tfrac{1}{3}\sqrt{1 + \sin 0.4} = 0.3929$$

$$x_2 = \tfrac{1}{3}\sqrt{1 + \sin 0.3929} = 0.391985$$

$$x_3 = \tfrac{1}{3}\sqrt{1 + \sin 0.391985} = 0.391865$$

$$x_4 = \tfrac{1}{3}\sqrt{1 + \sin 0.391865} = 0.391849$$

$$x_5 = \tfrac{1}{3}\sqrt{1 + \sin 0.391849} = 0.391847$$

$$x_6 = \tfrac{1}{3}\sqrt{1 + \sin 0.391847} = 0.391847$$

Thus we have obtained a solution to six decimal accuracy.

We have given a number of examples of iterative methods

[4]Note that the values of x_n are in radians, i.e., sin 0.4 means the sine of the angle whose measure is 0.4 radians.

in this chapter. In most cases the procedures are onerous if done with pencil and paper but very well suited to the rapid fifth-grade arithmetic of the computer.

Exercises

1. Solve the equation

$$x^2 - 3.6x - 7 = 0$$

for both roots by an iterative method.
2. Graph the successive values for one of the roots of exercise 1.
3. Use formula (6.7) to find $\sqrt{5}$ correct to ten decimals. Compare the work with previous methods for finding $\sqrt{5}$.
4. Use Ballantine's method to find $\sqrt[3]{721}$.
5. By graphing estimate the positive root of $2x - \cos x = 0$.
6. Using the estimate of exercise 5 as an initial value, devise an iterative procedure and find the root correct to five decimals.
7. Find the positive root of $x - e^x + 2 = 0$ correct to four decimals.

7. Relaxation Methods

The word "relaxation" has an intriguing sound, especially to someone who has been concentrating on the mathematics of the previous chapters. However, the word is used in a different sense here. It is used to describe a powerful method of computation—a method used with great success in England during the second World War.

In obtaining a solution by relaxation we perform a *large number of very simple* operations. During the 1940's Professor R. V. Southwell was able to solve some extremely complicated problems by training a large corps of students and women to do these simple operations. In fact it was he who first used the word relaxation.

A simple example will introduce the method and explain the origin of the word. Suppose that we have a string under uniform tension T and fixed at its end points. Suppose further that the string has 8 equal weights of mass m spaced along it at equal horizontal distances d. We may then ask what the equilibrium position of the weights will be under the forces of tension and gravity. In most physical problems it is necessary to make some simplifying assumptions in order that the problem may be solved by known methods. The present problem is no exception so that we assume that the mass of the string can be ignored and that the tension T is so large that in comparison the displacements of the weights are small. If, however, we exaggerate the sag in the string, we would have the diagram shown in Figure 11.

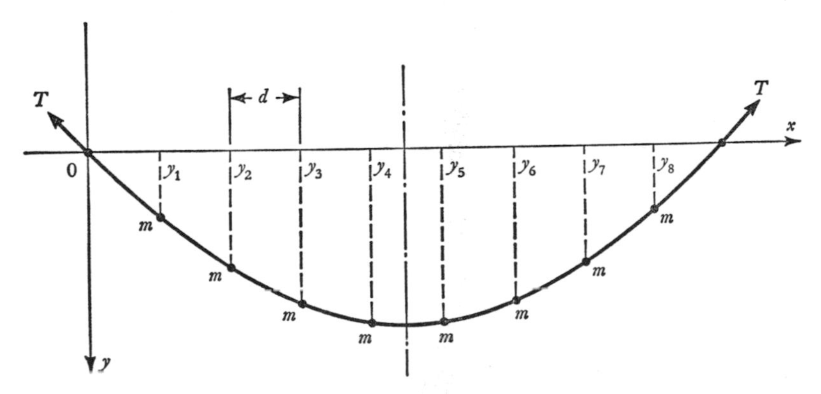

Fig. 11. Displacements in a string loaded with masses *m*.

By symmetry we have $y_1 = y_8$, $y_2 = y_7$, etc. If we concentrate our attention on the net upward force on the mass m_3, and choose our units so that $mgd/T = 1$, we have

$$-1 - y_2 + 2y_3 - y_4 = F_3 .$$

Similar expressions for the forces on the other masses gives us the following system of equations:

$$\begin{aligned}
-1 + 2y_1 - y_2 \qquad\qquad &= F_1 \\
-1 - y_1 + 2y_2 - y_3 \qquad &= F_2 \\
-1 \qquad - y_2 + 2y_3 - y_4 &= F_3 \\
-1 \qquad\qquad - y_3 + y_4 &= F_4
\end{aligned} \tag{7.1}$$

The desired equilibrium position in this case corresponds to the y's obtained by solving equations (7.1) with all the F's equal to zero. In this particular case the methods of high school algebra could produce a solution quite easily. If the number of equations is large, however, then it would be advantageous to seek other methods.

To solve the system (7.1) by the relaxation method we would first assign arbitrary values to y_1, y_2, y_3, and y_4. We would then substitute these values into (7.1) and calculate the F's. Ordinarily they would not be zero as required for equilibrium. The values of the F's are called *residuals* and the relaxation method seeks to bring these residuals to zero by correcting the initial guesses of the y's in a systematic manner.

Southwell thought of the F's as the negatives of the constraining forces which must actually be applied to the masses to keep the system in equilibrium with the particular displacements under consideration. Each step in the calculation is thus thought of as a relaxation of one of these external constraints—hence the term *relaxation.*

As an illustration[1] of the relaxation technique let us consider a pair of equations,

$$\begin{aligned} 3x - y &= 79 \\ x - 4y &= -212. \end{aligned} \tag{7.2}$$

These equations may be rewritten in the form

$$\begin{aligned} R_1 &\equiv 79 - 3x + y \\ R_2 &\equiv 212 + x - 4y \end{aligned} \tag{7.3}$$

where, for the *correct* values of x and y, the residuals R_1 and R_2 are both zero. For any other values of x and y the residuals are *not* zero but are a measure of the error of the solution. From (7.3) we can calculate R_1 and R_2 for any pair of x and y but we are interested in that unique pair which makes $R_1 = R_2 = 0$.

We begin by making an *operations table.* Looking at (7.3)

[1] See also Grad, E. M.: "Solution of Electrical Engineering Problems by Southwell's Relaxation Method," *Comm. and Elect.*, no. 1, pp. 205–214, July 1952.

we see that a unit positive change in x will change R_1 by -3 and R_2 by $+1$ and a unit positive change in y will change R_1 by $+1$ and R_2 by -4. Thus the operations table has the following form:[2]

Δx	Δy	ΔR_1	ΔR_2
1	0	-3	1
0	1	1	-4

This table is to be interpreted as follows: a positive unit change in x changes R_1 by -3 and R_2 by 1, etc.

Next we make an initial guess of x and y in order to start the computation. A good initial guess is desirable because it will shorten the subsequent numerical work, but it is by no means essential. In this particular example let us begin with $x = 0$ and $y = 0$ as initial values. Using these values we calculate R_1 and R_2 and enter these in a *relaxation table.*

Then we pick out the largest[3] residual (in this case 212) and reduce this to zero. A change of 53 in y will accomplish this. However, this will also change R_1 to 132. Next we reduce R_1 by making a change of 44 in x even though this brings R_2 back to 44. At this point the relaxation table has the following appearance:

x	y	R_1	R_2
0	0	79	212
	$\Delta y = 53$	132	0
$\Delta x = 44$		0	44

We continue by bringing the largest residual to zero each time until we have reached the desired degree of accuracy. In this example both residuals eventually reach zero, hence we

[2] The Greek letter Δ is used to designate a change in a variable. Thus a change in x is denoted by Δx, a change in R_1 by ΔR_1, etc.

[3] By "largest" we mean largest in absolute value.

have an exact solution. The finished relaxation table would have this appearance:

x	y	R_1	R_2
0	0	79	212
	$\Delta y = 53$	132	0
$\Delta x = 44$		0	44
	$\Delta y = 11$	11	0
$\Delta x = 4$		-1	4
	$\Delta y = 1$	0	0

Final values of the variables can be found by adding to the initial x and y all the changes that have been made, that is,

$$x = 0 + 44 + 4 = 48 \quad \text{and} \quad y = 0 + 53 + 11 + 1 = 65\,.$$

A check now shows that these values do indeed produce zero residuals.

$$R_1 = 79 - 144 + 65 = 0\,,$$

$$R_2 = 212 + 48 - 260 = 0\,.$$

Hence $x = 48$ and $y = 65$ are the values sought.

One of the advantages of the method is that it is self-correcting. If we had made an error at some point in the computation, the residuals R_1 and R_2 would not have become zero but would have some small values. We could take these as new starting values of the residuals which could then be "relaxed" to zero. The increments in x and y required to do this would be added to those previously obtained to give the correct solution.

Since the results can be checked easily during the progress of the work, it is better to work quickly and risk arithmetical errors, making checks of the residuals only occasionally, than to stop and check each step by which the residuals have been calculated. Of course, if the computation is done on a digital computer, errors would not occur unless there was a malfunction in the machine.

There are a number of devices by which the relaxation process can be speeded up. We note that in the previous example when one residual was *decreased*, the other was *increased* though by a smaller amount. If, therefore, instead of choosing an increment that will just make the largest residual zero, we use a *larger* increment, the work will be shortened. This over-compensation is known as *over-relaxation*. We can illustrate it by presenting an alternative method of working the last example.

x	y	R_1	R_2
0	0	79	212
	$\Delta y = 60$	139	−28
$\Delta x = 50$		−11	22
	$\Delta y = 5$	−6	2
$\Delta x = -2$		0	0
48	65		

Thus we arrive at the same result in fewer steps. It should be noted that over-relaxation is easier for the human operator than for the machine because its use requires the making of fairly complex decisions.

Another technique that can be used to speed up relaxation is known as *block relaxation*. This consists of applying the same increment to more than one of the variables at a time. In other words, it is a superposition of effects. We illustrate it by applying increments of 55 to both x and y in the last example.

x	y	R_1	R_2
0	0	79	212
$\Delta x = 55$	$\Delta y = 55$	−31	47
	$\Delta y = 10$	−21	7
$\Delta x = -7$		0	0
48	65		

Block relaxation works so well because it is easier to "liquidate" residuals that are of opposite sign than those that are all of the same sign. Note that after the residuals became -21 and 7 it was not even necessary to use over-relaxation.

Finally, we could have combined the last two steps of the previous example into one by working from the operations table. Applying unequal increments to more than one of the variables at a time is known as *group relaxation*. This technique is particularly useful if one residual is very large compared to the others.

We have seen that the relaxation method is self-correcting since *any* way that the residuals are brought to zero leads to the correct result. For machine computation, however, it is desirable to have constant checks at each step. A method of checking can be used that was originally suggested by Gauss.[4]

We illustrate Gauss' method by considering the pair of equations,

$$\begin{aligned} 6x - 2y &= 4.8, \\ -2x + 7y &= 26.9. \end{aligned} \tag{7.4}$$

If we make a change of variable so that the new variables z_1, z_2, and z_3 are related to the old by

$$\begin{aligned} x &= z_1 - z_3 \\ y &= z_2 - z_3, \end{aligned} \tag{7.5}$$

then (7.4) is transformed into

$$\begin{aligned} 6z_1 - 2z_2 - 4z_3 &= 4.8 \\ -2z_1 + 7z_2 - 9z_3 &= 26.9 \\ -4z_1 - 5z_2 + 13z_3 &= -31.7. \end{aligned} \tag{7.6}$$

Here the first two equations were obtained by substituting

[4] Carl Friedrich Gauss (1777–1855), a German mathematician and physicist, made important contributions to every branch of mathematics known in his day.

(7.5) into (7.4). The third equation is merely the negative of the sum of the first two.

The consequence of this transformation is that at every stage of the relaxation process, the sum of the residuals must be *zero*. The check at each step therefore consists of summing the residuals, and only at the end of the calculation need the final result be checked by substitution into the original set of equations. Although the extra equation increases the burden of relaxation, this extra work becomes relatively smaller as the number of equations is increased. With a computer doing the arithmetic one additional equation doesn't make much difference and the slight increase in computing time is easily offset by the convenience of the check.

It is natural to ask if the relaxation method will work for every set of linear equations. The answer is yes and no. There are many sets for which the method will not work but such sets can be recognized and transformed into a form for which the method will work.[5]

Consider the set of equations

$$\begin{aligned} 4x - 5y &= 3 \\ 2x + 4y &= 8 \end{aligned} \tag{7.7}$$

which has the solution $x = 2$ and $y = 1$. No matter how we begin or what we try, the residuals do not become smaller as we apply more operations. However if we multiply each equation by the coefficient of its first term and add them, and then multiply each by the coefficient of the second term and add, we obtain

$$\begin{aligned} 5x - 3y &= 7 \\ -12x + 41y &= 17\,. \end{aligned} \tag{7.8}$$

For these equations, which have the same solution as (7.7), the method works. The difference between the two sets is

[5] Squire, William: "Relaxation Methods," *Math. Mag.* (33), no. 4, pp. 177–183, March–April 1960.

simple. In the first set the coefficient of y was larger (in absolute value) than the coefficient of x in both equations. In the second set the coefficient of x was larger than that of y in one equation and the opposite condition held in the other.

Relaxation methods are useful not only in solving sets of simultaneous linear algebraic equations such as we have discussed but also in solving ordinary and partial differential equations. The method is especially useful for solving equations governing the flow of heat in a body and for determining the electric and magnetic fields in regions bounded by irregular boundaries. These problems are not discussed because they require more advanced knowledge of calculus and differential equations.

Exercises

1. Make an operations table for the pair of equations given in (7.8).
2. Solve (7.8) by the relaxation method.
3. Solve the following system by the relaxation method:

$$\begin{cases} x + y - 3z = 11 \\ x + 3y - z = 13 \\ 3x + y - z = 11 \end{cases}$$

4. Solve by relaxation:

$$\begin{cases} x - 4y + z = 11 \\ 3x - 5z + 2w = 13 \\ 2x - y + 3z - w = 9 \\ 8x + y + 4z - 2w = 30 \end{cases}$$

8. Monte Carlo Methods

To mathematicians a "Monte Carlo Method" is not a way of "breaking the bank" but a way of attacking a complex problem. The method itself dates back at least a few centuries, although the name is a fairly recent one.

Fundamentally, the method consists of determining probabilities in certain complex situations by playing a game of chance. In order to obtain dependable results, it is essential that the game be played many times; hence the method is definitely computer-oriented.

Chance processes play a role in almost all phases of modern life—the flow of traffic, the operation of a communication system, the demand made on a central power supply, etc. Accurate analysis and prediction in many cases is made difficult or impossible by the chance fluctuations that occur.

Physicists have found that certain problems, mainly in connection with statistical mechanics, particle diffusion, and similar problems do not yield very easily to classical analysis. In these cases numerical solutions can be obtained most easily by considering a *probabilistic model* of the system. In other words, instead of analyzing the system as a whole, we can concentrate our attention on the behavior of a large number of individual particles. These particles, of course, exhibit random behavior in accordance with the model we have chosen. By tracing the histories of a *large number* of individual particles we can draw meaningful conclusions about the *whole* system. Considering each particle history as a separate experiment, the statistical average of many experiments will give the necessary information about the system.

As a simple illustration of a Monte Carlo method consider the case of the poker player who has determined the probability of filling an inside straight. Although he may not understand probability theory he has arrived at a fairly definite answer, perhaps the hard way. That is to say, he has performed a large number of experiments over a period of years, some of which were successful and some which were not. His knowledge of the probability figure is thus a statistical average of his past experiences.

To show how a game of chance can produce a useful result let us look at the simplest imaginable game. Suppose that we wish to obtain the product of two proper fractions, $\frac{5}{8}$ and $\frac{3}{14}$. We can devise a game to perform this multiplication by marking two packs of cards containing, respectively, 8 and 14 cards. We put a distinguishing mark on 5 of the cards in the first pack and another mark on 3 of the cards in the second pack. Next we shuffle the cards in each pack separately in order to introduce chance or randomness. Each play of the game (or each experiment) consists of drawing a card from each pack and noting whether or not both cards are marked. If both cards are marked, we score one point, if not, we score zero. After each play we return the cards to their respective packs and shuffle. Our final score is the total number of points divided by the total number of trials.

When we draw a card from the first pack, the probability that it will be marked is $\frac{5}{8}$. Similarly, the probability of drawing a marked card from the second deck is $\frac{3}{14}$. Since drawing cards from the two packs are classed as "independent events," the theory of probability indicates that the probability of drawing marked cards from *both* decks is the product $\frac{5}{8} \times \frac{3}{14}$. If the draws are made at random and if the number of trials is large, the average score should approach this value. In other words, if we play this game 1000 times, we would expect that approximately 134 points would be recorded because $\frac{5}{8} \times \frac{3}{14} \doteq 0.134$.

This method of obtaining the product of two numbers is perhaps the most laborious that one can imagine. An extension of the same idea, however, can be used to solve large systems of linear equations. The number of steps involved is enormous when considered from the human point of view but quite routine for the computer. Furthermore the computer is not subject to errors resulting from boredom.

Let us look at another problem that can be solved by a Monte Carlo method. Suppose we wish to find the area enclosed by some irregular boundary. One way to do this is to draw the figure on graph paper and count the little squares inside the boundary. By counting partial squares at the boundary carefully, we could get quite an accurate result.

Instead of counting squares we might proceed in the following unorthodox fashion.[1] We could place our finger at random on the sheet of paper on which the drawing is made. Only one of four things can happen: (1) our finger will land *inside* the boundary, (2) our finger will land *outside* the boundary, (3) our finger will land *on* the boundary, or (4) our finger will miss the paper entirely. This time we would score one point for the first case and zero for the second case. We would not score anything for the third or fourth cases. The final result would then be obtained by multiplying the area of the paper by a fraction whose numerator is the sum of points and whose denominator is the total number of points *and* zeros recorded.

Again the accuracy depends on two things—a large number of trials and true randomness in placing our finger down. Thus

[1] Strong, C. L.: "An Excursion into the Problem of Measuring Irregular Areas," *Scient. Amer.* (199), no. 2, pp. 107–108, August 1958.

the characteristics of a Monte Carlo method are many trials of an experiment involving randomness. The large number of repetitions does not present any problem to the digital computer but the matter of randomesss does.

Strictly speaking, the random number exists only as the result of a random process. Thus a *perfect* roulette wheel could serve to supply random numbers. The catch is that not only is it impossible to build a perfect wheel but the maintenance of such a device would be extremely difficult. Any mechanical device is subject to wear and this wear introduces a bias in favor of certain numbers.

Electronic methods have been used to obtain random numbers. The thermionic noise, i.e. static, of a vacuum tube has been used to trigger a counter. In this way lists of random numbers were obtained. These numbers have actually been *tested* for randomness. This may sound peculiar but in a list of random numbers one would expect to find as many odd numbers as even ones. One would also expect approximately even distribution of the ten numerals 0, 1, 2, $\cdots$, 9. Other similar tests are used to insure "true" randomness.

For a time it was thought that the digits in irrational numbers such as π and e (the base of natural logarithms) were random. For this reason these numbers were calculated to many decimal places. The number π, for example, has been computed to 100,000 decimal places.[2] A study of the first 10,000 of these[3], however, showed that the digits were *not* truly random. The number e is being computed to one million digits and tests of randomness will be made on these.

It would seem that having a good list of random numbers available is all that is needed to solve problems by the Monte Carlo technique. Unfortunately, it is not efficient to use such a list with a computer. Reading in a lot of numbers is too slow,

[2] Shanks, Daniel and Wrench, J. T.: "Calculation of π to 100,000 Decimals," *Math. of Comp.* (16), no. 77, p. 76, January 1962.

[3] Pathria, R. K.: "A Statistical Study of Randomness Among the First 10,000 Digits of π," *Math. of Comp.* (16), no. 78, pp. 188–197, April 1962.

storing the numbers is too wasteful of needed storage space in the computer, and large problems often require more numbers than have been published. (It is not possible to double the size of a table by reading it twice, just as you cannot read a book by reading the first page over and over).

Thus it is desirable to *generate* random numbers in the computer as they are needed. This overcomes the previous objections and has the added advantage that computations may be repeated exactly, a procedure sometimes needed for checking. Numbers generated by the computer are sometimes called *pseudo-random* because they are subject to the limitations of the computer. In a list of truly random numbers, for example, one would expect to find numbers containing more digits than can be obtained in the computer.

It was originally von Neumann[4] who suggested the following scheme for obtaining pseudo-random numbers on a computer. One takes an n-digit number, squares it and uses the middle n digits as a random number. This is in turn squared and the process continues in this manner. Although this method is simplicity itself, it has a serious drawback. There is no way of knowing ahead of time whether the numbers will begin repeating after a certain point. In fact, it has been estimated[5] that sequences of such numbers would not exceed 100,000 without repetition. Large problems often need more numbers than this.

A number of methods have been developed for generating random numbers on a computer. Most of these require less computing time than the mid-square method just described and they produce reliable results which can be repeated.

One of the important problems faced by modern physicists is the problem of analysis of the attenuation of neutrons. The problem here is to determine what happens when a large number of neutrons having a certain energy are released in a certain

[4] John von Neumann (1903–1957), one of the foremost mathematicians of this century, was a pioneer in considering the design and possibilities of high-speed computing devices.

[5] Hammer, Preston C.: Private Communication, March 20, 1964.

direction. Since it is impossible to analyze the problem as a whole, the physicist fixes his attention on a single neutron. This neutron can be assigned an energy and a direction from the allowable energies and directions but in a random manner. Another random number determines where the neutron will make its first collision, still another random number will determine the type of collision, that is, whether the neutron will be absorbed or scattered. If it is scattered, then there are two possibilities—it can be scattered elastically or inelastically. If it is scattered, we can assign a new direction and energy and repeat the whole process. These various steps can be repeated until the neutron is (1) absorbed, (2) attenuated to negligible energy, (3) reflected, or (4) transmitted. Considering that the various possibilities can occur in a random manner makes the problem an ideal one for a Monte Carlo method.

Another method which is based on probability and which is useful in solving many problems is known as the random-walk technique. Although it resembles quite closely the erratic meanderings of an inebriate, it produces quite accurate answers. We explain the method by means of a somewhat artificial problem.

Suppose we have a rectangular metal plate, and we keep the edges at constant temperatures (Figure 12). The top and bottom are kept at 0°, the left edge at 5° and the right edge at 10°. We carefully avoid saying anything about the temperatures at the four corners.

If we maintain the edge temperatures at the values shown for a long time, then the temperature at *any* point inside the rectangle will reach some fixed value. We say that the temperatures have reached a *steady-state condition.* Along the center line shown in Figure 12 we would expect the temperature to be very close to 5° just inside the left edge and very close to 10° just inside the right edge. Between these two points we would expect to find points where the temperature was 6°, 7°, 8° and 9°—the last at a point near the right edge.

Suppose now that we wish to find the temperature at some

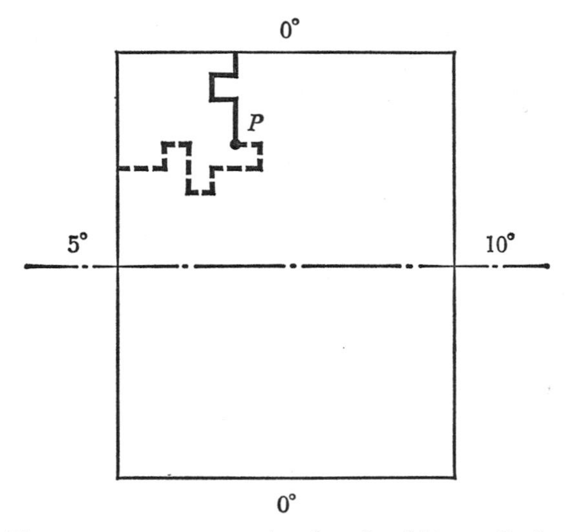

Fig. 12. Temperature at a point by the Monte Carlo method.

arbitrary point P of the plate. Starting at P we take a random walk which will end as soon as we reach an edge. We define a random walk as a series of unit steps in the horizontal and vertical directions. Two such walks are shown on Figure 11, one solid and one dotted. It is essential that steps be taken in the four possible directions in a random manner.

Since each random walk ends at a boundary, we record the temperature of the boundary. Thus, for the first walk (solid line) we record 0°, for the second walk (dotted line) we record 5°, etc. After many hundreds (perhaps thousands) of trials we find that we have recorded a great many zeros and a great many fives and not very many tens. The arithmetic average of all these will be a good indication of the temperature at the point P. Starting our random walks from this point, there is a greater probability of reaching the 0° and 5° edges than the 10° edge. But this is just another way of saying that the temperature at the point P depends more on the temperatures of the left and top edges than it does on the temperature of the right edge.

To find the temperature at some other point of the plate

we would use *that* point as the starting point of a *new* series of random walks. This method is ideally suited to a computer since it requires many random walks and the results of these have to be averaged.

Exercises

1. Using the technique described in this chapter, find the product of $\frac{8}{9}$ and $\frac{11}{24}$. (Hint: Use ordinary playing cards, 9 of one suit and 24 of another.)
2. Find the product of $\frac{1}{3}$ and $\frac{1}{4}$ and compare the accuracy obtained with that in Exercise 1.
3. Can you suggest some ways of obtaining random numbers? (Hint: Consider telephone numbers, addresses, automobile license numbers, etc.)
4. Start with any four-digit number and using the mid-squaring method obtain ten random numbers. Test these for randomness by using the most obvious tests.

9. Some Special Techniques

In numerical work we frequently lose a great deal of time by recording partial results. This can be avoided by making a concise arrangement of the calculations. Lánczos[1] suggested a device which is of great help in many algorithms. His method involves the use of a "movable strip" and can be explained in terms of desk calculations although the technique can be easily coded for digital computers also.

A certain fixed set of numbers is written down on a vertical strip of paper. This movable column then operates on another given column, called the "fixed strip." The operation consists of multiplying two adjacent numbers, one from the fixed strip, the other from the movable strip. The partial products are summed (mentally) and the results are written on a third strip called the "nascent (or developed) strip." As the movable strip moves downward one step, the operation is repeated and the next element of the nascent strip is obtained. When the movable strip arrives at the bottom of the fixed strip, the process ends.

[1] Cornelius Lánczos (1893–), numerical analyst and applied mathematician.

The following simple scheme illustrates the method.

Movable strip	Fixed strip	Nascent strip
−3		
−2		
4		
1	2	2
↓	−3	5
	−5	−21
	0	−20
	1	20

This kind of arrangement is encountered in the weighting of data, numerical differentiation of a function, etc. Note that here the numbers of the nascent strip have no influence on the later operations. In other words, we could have obtained the nascent column by starting the movable strip from the bottom and moving upward or in any other sequence.

A variation of the above method occurs quite frequently, however, in which the nascent strip is put between the movable strip and the fixed strip. A "feedback" arrangement of this kind must be performed in the proper sequence. The movable strip now operates on the nascent strip and only the lowest element of the movable strip reaches over to the fixed strip.

The following example shows how this second algorithm operates.

Movable strip	Nascent strip	Fixed strip
−3		
−2		
4		
1	2	2
↓	5	−3
	11	−5
	28	0
	76	1

This is the arrangement used in the division of polynomials. We can demonstrate this technique by dividing the polynomial

$$f(x) = 1.09375x^3 + 1.0625x^2 - 0.3x - 1$$

by $x - 0.79$. This is equivalent to determining whether or not $x_0 = 0.79$ is a root of the polynomial equation $f(x) = 0$. In this case we are interested in the remainder resulting from this division. If the remainder is zero, then 0.79 is a root.

The division can be done by putting 0.79 and 1 in the movable strip and the coefficients of $f(x)$ into the fixed strip. We thus obtain the following:

Movable strip	Nascent strip	Fixed strip	Remainder
0.79			
1	1.09375	1.09375	
↓	1.92656	1.0625	
	1.22198	−0.3	
	0	−1	−0.03463

Note that instead of writing the last element of the nascent strip, i.e., −0.03463, we transferred this result to the remainder column and filled out the last element of the nascent strip with zero.

The movable strip technique can also be employed for the division of one polynomial by another. Suppose we wish to divide

$$A(x) = 6x^6 - 3x^5 + x^3 - x^2$$

by

$$B(x) = x^3 + 2x^2 + 4x - 1 .$$

We write the coefficients of $A(x)$ starting with the coefficient of the term having highest degree and ending with the lowest. If a certain power of x is missing, we write zero for its coefficient. In this way we obtain the fixed strip.

In using this method, the coefficient of the term having

highest degree in the denominator must be normalized to 1. This can always be done by introducing the appropriate multiplier into the numerator and denominator of the original fraction. The coefficients of $B(x)$ are written on a movable strip, starting with 1 and moving *upward.* The sign of each coefficient is also reversed with the exception of the highest coefficient 1 which remains unchanged.

Now the movable strip technique generates the quotient of $A(x)$ and $B(x)$ as follows:

$B(x)$	Quotient	$A(x)$	Remainder
1	6	6	
−4	−15	−3	
−2	6	0	
1	55	1	
↓	0	−1	−150
	0	0	−214
	0	0	55

Hence

$$\frac{6x^6 - 3x^5 + x^3 - x^2}{x^3 + 2x^2 + 4x - 1}$$

$$= 6x^3 - 15x^2 + 6x + 55 + \frac{-150x^2 - 214x + 55}{x^3 + 2x^2 + 4x - 1}.$$

Another technique used in computer work, and also generally useful, is concerned with the evaluation of polynomials. It can be illustrated by considering an approximation to the sine of an angle,

$$\sin x \doteq x - \frac{x^3}{6} + \frac{x^5}{120}. \tag{9.1}$$

This formula can be used in different ways and with differing resultant accuracy.

Given a positive value of x we can form the various terms on the right of (9.1) and combine them to obtain $\sin x$. Such a direct calculation requires two divisions, three multiplications, one addition and one subtraction. These operations can be more conveniently done if we rewrite (9.1) in the equivalent form,

$$\sin x \doteq [(\tfrac{1}{120}x^2 - \tfrac{1}{6})x^2 + 1]x\,. \tag{9.2}$$

This form is called the *nested polynomial* form. The accuracy of the computation is also improved in this way. In the first instance the round-off error may be as much as 1.5 in the last place while in the second the greatest error will be 0.5 in the last place. It may also happen that fewer operations are required when a polynomial is evaluated in the nested form.

If a polynomial is to be evaluated for many values of the variable which are regularly spaced, it may be better to build up the function from differences. This procedure can best be illustrated by a numerical example.

Suppose we wish to tabulate the polynomial

$$P(x) = 2x^4 - 5x^3 - 8x^2 + 17x + 2$$

for[2] $x = 0(1)10$. We find the successive differences of $P(x)$ as follows:

$$\begin{aligned}
\Delta P(x) &\equiv P(x+1) - P(x) \\
&= 2(x+1)^4 - 5(x+1)^3 - 8(x+1)^2 + 17(x+1) \\
&\qquad + 2 - P(x) \\
&= 8x^3 - 3x^2 - 23x + 6 \\
\Delta^2 P(x) &= 8(x+1)^3 - 3(x+1)^2 - 23(x+1) + 6 \\
&\qquad - 8x^3 + 3x^2 + 23x - 6 \\
&= 24x^2 + 18x - 18 \\
\Delta^3 P(x) &= 24(x+1)^2 + 18(x+1) - 18 - 24x^2 - 18x + 18 \\
&= 48x + 42
\end{aligned}$$

[2] The notation $x = 0(1)10$ means, "give x values starting with $x = 0$ and ending with $x = 10$, and going in steps of 1."

$$\Delta^4 P(x) = 48(x+1) + 42 - 48x - 42$$
$$= 48$$
$$\Delta^5 P(x) = 0.$$

Next we evaluate the above differences at the first value of x that we will use, that is, for $x = 0$. This gives

$$\Delta_0 P(x) = 6, \quad \Delta_0^2 P(x) = -18, \quad \Delta_0^3 P(x) = 42, \quad \Delta_0^4 P(x) = 48. \tag{9.3}$$

Knowing these leading differences of $P(x)$ now enables us to construct a difference table which will give all the required information. Note than in this case the fourth difference is a constant (does not depend on x) while all higher differences are zero. This is characteristic of a polynomial of fourth degree.[3]

The following table was built by starting with the constant fourth differences and the other leading differences (9.3) and working from these to the left and to the bottom.

x	$P(x)$	$\Delta P(x)$	$\Delta^2 P(x)$	$\Delta^3 P(x)$	$\Delta^4 P(x)$
0	2				
		6			
1	8		−18		
		−12		42	
2	−4		24		48
		12		90	
3	8		114		48
		126		138	
4	134		252		48
		378		186	
5	512		438		48
		816		234	

[3] It should be mentioned that differences can be taken even though the difference between successive x-values is not unity. If the x's differ by h, we have the general definition, $\Delta P(x) = P(x+h) - P(x)$.

x	$P(x)$	$\Delta P(x)$	$\Delta^2 P(x)$	$\Delta^3 P(x)$	$\Delta^4 P(x)$
6	1328		672		48
		1488		282	
7	2816		954		48
		2442		330	
8	5258		1284		48
		3726		378	
9	8984		1662		
		5388			
10	14372				

We can obtain considerable information from the above table. We can read off the values of $P(x)$ for various values of x. For example, $P(3) = 8$, $P(7) = 2816$, etc. We also notice that the polynomial equation $P(x) = 0$ has a root between $x = 1$ and $x = 2$ and another between $x = 2$ and $x = 3$. If necessary we can also extend the table in either direction to obtain values for x greater than 10 and for negative values of x. These extensions require only the operation of subtraction while the original table required only addition.

Exercises

1. Divide $x^3 - 12x + 3$ by (a) $x - 3$, (b) $x - 3.1$, (c) $x - 3.2$.
2. Divide $8x^3 - 18x^2 + 11x - 6$ by $4x^2 - 3x + 2$.
3. Write the polynomial $3x^4 - 2x^3 + x^2 - x + 7$ in nested form.
4. Find the differences of the polynomial of Exercise 3 using an interval of 1.
5. Evaluate the polynomial of Exercise 3 for $x = 0(1)10$.

10. Computer Applications—Present and Future

It seems fitting to conclude by discussing some of the general problems being solved on computers. We must remember, however, that many of the general problems require one or more of the specialized techniques discussed in previous chapters.

One of the best sources of complex problems is the field of *operations research.* This field develops mathematical models which simulate certain large-scale operations. Before a satisfactory model can be developed, it is often necessary to perform certain controlled experiments. Hence, in a sense, operations research is an experimental science, just like physics and chemistry.

The difficulty is that in most operations it is not easy to persuade the people in charge to make experiments. They may be perfectly willing to permit experimentation on the various individual operations which make up the whole, but it is nearly always impossible to experiment with the entire system. Imagine the reaction of a military staff to a proposal to try out a completely new form of landing operation or a new method of issuing supplies. Or imagine the response of bank officials to a suggestion that a completely new system of routing and recording bank deposits and withdrawals be tried out for an entire month.

Thus one of the difficulties in making an accurate model of a large operation is that it must be based on *meager* experimental evidence. Another difficulty is that in a complex operation there are too many possibilities that need to be checked. Hence the design of the mathematical model can best be done with the aid of a computer.

Once we know the behavior of the individual operations and the external influences on the whole system, these behaviors can be simulated by the computer, and the various interactions can be programmed so that the computer will simulate the whole operation satisfactorily. The various uncertainties can be introduced by Monte Carlo methods; the various rules of operation which interconnect the elements can be programmed, and the results can be presented in a way that will indicate the changes resulting from the application of new rules.

As an illustration of the type of simulation that is under discussion, consider the following problem which was analyzed at the Massachusetts Institute of Technology Computation Center.[1] This study had to do with the spare parts supply system of Army Ordnance—one of the largest supply systems in the world. There is a complex sequence of supply levels, main depots in this country, and smaller depots—some abroad—which furnish material to the supply stations for the various forces. Requests for parts come to the supply sergeant, who fills them from stock, if possible. As his stock becomes low he requests replenishment from a depot, which in turn replenishes from another depot or from the manufacturer. The rules of operation govern such things as the size of the replenishment order, where it is sent, and how it is related to the size of the inventory remaining.

The analysis of this problem began with a study of data

[1] Langer, R. E. (editor): *Frontiers of Numerical Mathematics*, Chapter 5, "Operations Research," by Philip M. Morse, U. of Wisc. Press, 1960.

from the demands for spare parts for five years of operation. This led to a knowledge of the statistics of the demand fluctuations. It was also found that the many thousands of kinds of items could be reduced to 50 in regard to size, value, demand rate, and variance of demand rate.

A model was developed which could be run on the computer and which represented an equivalent year of operation in a few minutes. The conditions and rules of the previous five years were inserted and the output was studied to make certain that the model *did* simulate the reactions and fluctuations that were known to exist. When satisfactory agreement was reached, the rules of operation were changed to see if the stock-out time could be reduced. In order to check the new rules for sensitivity, the statistical pattern of demands was changed and the results noted.

In this analysis all the experimentation had to be performed on the computer. Nevertheless, results were obtained which indicated what type of supply system was the best under certain conditions.

Another kind of operation which has been simulated on a computer has been automobile traffic. The behavior of traffic is a very complex operation considering all the variabilities of driver reaction. Hence it was advisable to begin with the simplest case, that of one-lane traffic with no turning out for passing, such as might occur in a tunnel.

Each driver was assigned a maximum speed, a reaction time, and he was programmed to accelerate or decelerate according to the relative speed and distance between his car and the one ahead. These factors were varied from car to car. The first simulation had so many factors and so much variability that it ran on the computer only about five times as fast as the actual traffic. Also there were many more rear-end collisions than actually occur in a tunnel. The program was modified and simplified, so that eventually it ran much more rapidly and represented the real situation more faithfully.

Having a program which simulates known traffic behavior

makes it possible to conduct experiments which cannot be done with actual traffic. For example, the effect of a "drunk driver" (one having an abnormally long reaction time) could be traced. It was also possible to observe the effect of speed limits on the number of accidents and also on the mean rate of flow of cars through the tunnel.

Another example of simulation, even more complex than the last two, is a study of economic forecasting. The information here is really meager, because only once in ten years do we have reliable information concerning the economic status of the nation. This comes as a result of the U. S. census which can be thought of as an instantaneous snapshot of the national economy. After another ten years we have another snapshot but there is no way to obtain a direct correlation between the two. Accurate forecasting would necessitate a *detailed* knowledge of individuals over the ten-year period—their marriages, deaths, job changes, economic interactions, etc.

Obviously it is impractical actually to observe enough people continuously. The computer, however, can be programmed for a machine simulation which corresponds to the gross changes as measured by consecutive census figures. A typical group of 2000 persons was chosen, appropriately distributed in age, marital, and economic status, to simulate census data for a town. This hypothetical town could be considered as a cross-section of the total population. Each of the 2000 persons was then checked each month by a Monte Carlo process to determine whether he got a raise, whether he got married or bought a car or a refrigerator or a house. His status was modified accordingly and the effect of this change on others was calculated.

Some of the factors had to be guessed and some changed later in order that the figures at the end of the ten-year run would correspond to the next census figures. This particular program was so complex that a ten-year history took about ten hours to run on the computer.

Combinations of the problems previously discussed occur

quite often in business. Here it is essential to analyze situations concerned with returns on investment, budgeting, forecasting, manufacturing-distribution patterns, and production scheduling. Problems in these areas are usually characterized by the fact that only small amounts of data are available and yet many computations must be made.

The successful solution of business problems is generally responsible for the profit the business can show. A large food manufacturer, for example, can save half million dollars a year by finding the most economical shipping pattern that can be used to move its products from factory to warehouses.

Analyzing complex systems on the basis of meager data is a challenge to the mathematician. By using computers he can model events in the real world and sometimes solve problems by trial and error. He can experiment with the aid of the computer and refine his model so that it is the best that can be designed with the data at hand.

There is an even greater challenge than that resulting from insufficient data. In some cases the data *fluctuates*—and in a random manner! Examples of this can be found in queueing (or waiting-line) problems. This situation exists when the demands for service and the time required to provide the service vary. Aircraft waiting for landing clearance, production-line machinery waiting for repairs, and customers waiting for service can be classified as queueing problems. A computer can model these problems, and the effect of changes can be studied. A branch of mathematics, called "queueing theory," has been developed to deal with problems of this kind. Here, too, the computer is invaluable because of the large number of cases that have to be studied and because of the randomness of the data.

Another type of problem has led to the development of "mathematical programming" theory. The simplest problems in this area are known as *linear programming* problems. These problems arise in situations where it is necessary to blend various components into a single product which meets certain specifications. Examples are found in producing gasoline, cattle feeds, fertilizers and alloys. It is not good business to produce final products whose quality exceeds the specifications by very much. With the aid of a computer it is possible to find the most economical mixture that will meet requirements.

To some extent a homemaker is faced with this problem in the preparation of meals. It is certainly an important problem to the dietitian of a hospital. She must determine what foods to buy, and in what quantities, in order that all the necessary nutrients and vitamins be supplied each patient and, at the same time, the total cost is a minimum. The computer serves in many and varied areas!

Another difficult problem exists today because of what has been called the "information explosion." So many technical articles are being written that obtaining information on a certain topic is becoming a serious problem. When a scientist finds eight references on some new subject, he cannot be sure if he has found eight of the ten existing ones or eight of the eight hundred. Here we are faced with an *information retrieval* problem. The information is somewhere, but the question is, how are we to obtain it? Again the computer may come to the rescue. Some work is being done in which computers are used to write abstracts of technical articles. If these abstracts are put on magnetic tape, then the computer can be used to find certain information. The situation is analogous to our asking thousands of librarians to help us find published material on a certain topic.

The computer is also useful in designing new products and systems. Many firms have small computers which their engineers use to make a preliminary design which is then refined. This method results in a great savings of time and money because different designs can be tried on the computer. Here the designs are mathematical and, if they don't work, it is necessary only to change some numbers—no costly production is involved. In designing a twin-engine jet aircraft, for example, if was found that a certain wing configuration was stable only if the engines were mounted forty feet ahead of the wing. Obviously, this was not a practical solution and some modifications had to be made.

Changes to the mathematical model were accomplished quite easily on the computer.

Automobile manufacturers have carried the design problem several steps further. They are interested not only in the design of a car or truck—a static problem—but also in such items of performance as acceleration, fuel economy and riding characteristics. These are dynamic situations and increase the complexity of the mathematical model. It is not possible to represent by a set of equations all that happens when a car moves down the road. It is now necessary to use combinations of theoretical equations, empirical equations and tabular data to describe how the various parts of the car behave. Then all this information must be tied together to produce a unified whole—the moving car. In other words, from all the variables that are present in this complex situation, it is necessary to choose *one* as the independent variable. A convenient and meaningful independent variable is time.

The analysis can proceed in innumerable ways; this fact, again, brings the capabilities of the computer into the picture. For example, at a given instant a uniform acceleration can be given to the car. The effect of this can be followed through successive increments of time to determine what happens to engine performance, fuel economy, riding smoothness, etc. If we had computers of immense storage ability and great computing speed and if we knew more about the characteristics of materials subjected to heat, abrasion, vibration, stress, etc., we could model a car so faithfully that we could represent the conditions that exist during a typical lifetime of the car and study the wear on a certain part during this period. Perhaps we could even predict when the part would fail. The ability to model a real-life system this way would lead to the design of safer, as well as more economical, cars.

In spite of the high speed at which modern computers operate, complex problems such as the last one described require an inordinate amount of computer time. As faster computers are designed, computer designers are running into serious problems. One of these has to do with the upper limit of the speed with which electrical signals can flow (186,000 miles per second). Some computers have such high computing speeds that this limitation becomes an important factor, so that wires have to be kept as short as possible and the whole computer miniaturized.

Since there is a limit to how small a computer can be, it is apparent that other means must be found to increase the speed of computation. One method that has been discussed[2] in recent years is that of *parallel computation.* Most of our mathematics is arranged in such a way that the work proceeds *serially.* In other words, one step must be completed before the next dependent step can be begun. This means that it is not possible to convert extra computing capacity into significantly greater speed. Hence the question has been asked, "Can a given computation be subdivided into independent sections which may be performed simultaneously?" This, of course, means an entirely new method of computation, perhaps a new form of arithmetic.

So far some work has been done toward achieving parallelism by the use of "modular arithmetic." Modular arithmetic,[3] when applicable, also has the added advantage of being free from round-off errors. Moreover, addition and multiplication in this system are carry-free.

Computer-oriented mathematics is in its infancy. Many new methods, especially suited to computers, are being developed. Some of these represent an advanced degree of mathematical sophistication. Some, on the other hand, are quite unsophisticated and are derived from methods used by early civilizations. The field is open to one and all—professional and amateur alike!

[2] Shapiro, H. S.: "Some Remarks on Modular Arithmetic and Parallel Computation," *Math. of Comp.* (16), No. 78, pp. 218–222, April 1962.

[3] Some examples of modular arithmetic are the "clock arithmetic" and the "egg-timer arithmetic" of certain elementary texts. Modular arithmetic is also known as a "residue number arithmetic."

11. Bibliography for Further Study

It often happens that during the early years of development of any technical field a great deal of material is published by and for the advanced worker. Only later do we begin to see articles for the general public—the tutorial articles. This is also true of computers and computer mathematics. The following references, however, may be helpful to one who desires to explore to a greater depth than was possible here.

Books

The Nature of Number by Roy Dubisch; The Ronald Press Company, New York, 1952.

A readable account of the history of our number system. It also discusses number systems other than the decimal.

Digital Computer Principles by Wayne C. Irwin; D. Van Nostrand Company Inc., Princeton, New Jersey, 1960.

This book was written for the person who wishes to become acquainted with digital computers, but who has a nontechnical background.

Bibliography for Further Study

Calculus—an Introductory Approach by Ivan Niven; D. Van Nostrand Company Inc., Princeton, New Jersey, 1961.

The first few chapters of this book are recommended to those who would like to know "what calculus is all about."

Mathematics and Computers by George R. Stibitz and Jules A. Larrivee; McGraw-Hill Book Company, Inc., New York, 1957.

This book discusses computers from the design viewpoint as well as the usage viewpoint. It also contains an extensive bibliography of over 200 references on computers and computer applications.

Computer Language—an Autoinstructional Introduction to Fortran by Harry L. Colman and Clarence Smallwood; McGraw-Hill Book Company, Inc., New York, 1962.

This is a programmed text which can be advantageously used by persons of widely varying technical backgrounds to learn a computer language. The Fortran system is a simple one and is also one of the most widely used.

Elementary Mathematics—a Logical Approach by Paul Sanders; International Textbook Company, Scranton, Pa., 1963.

A book which might be especially useful for the person who needs to review mathematics in preparation for working with computers or studying numerical methods. Recommended also for the general reader.

Numerical Analysis by Nathaniel Macon; John Wiley and Sons, Inc., New York, 1963.

A brief (approximately 150 pages) but thorough treatment of the subject for the reader with some knowledge of calculus. Recommended for self-study as the exposition is very good.

Fundamentals of Numerical Analysis by Augustus H. Fox; The Ronald Press Company, New York, 1963.

There are about 100 pages of very readable text here. The first half of the book requires practically no calculus.

Automatic Data-Processing Systems by Robert H. Gregory and Richard

L. Van Horn; Wadsworth Publishing Company, Inc., Belmont, California, 1960.

This is a very complete book describing computers, programming, data processing systems, systems design, and equipment acquisition. It is written for the reader with a non-technical background. An excellent reference book.

Articles

"On Popular Methods and Extant Problems in the Solution of Polynomial Equations" by Donald Greenspan; *Mathematics Magazine*, Vol. 31, no. 5, pp. 239–253, 1957.

With the advent of modern computational devices, new procedures for solving polynomial equations have emerged and older ones, once considered folly, have entered into the realm of practicality. This paper reviews many excellent methods of solving polynomial equations and contains an extensive bibliography of 61 references on the subject.

"Numerical Analysis and High School Mathematics" by Yudell L. Luke; *Mathematics Teacher*, Vol. 50, no. 7, pp. 507–512, November, 1957.

"Relaxation Methods" by William Squire; *Mathematics Magazine*, Vol. 33, no. 4, pp. 177–183, March–April, 1960.

Index

Index

Index